Language Issues

Issues

A course for advanced learners

Scott Thornbury

Contents chart

Talking effectively	Vocabulary	Writing
Rhythm	Word field: memory	Diagnosis
Stress in compound adjectives	Compound adjectives	Sequencers
Stressed and unstressed *would*	Compound nouns	Sequencers in narrative writing
Stress on nouns and verbs	Idioms: *rule*	Spelling rules
The sounds /ɪ/ and /aɪ/	Idioms: *chance*	Sequencers
Stressed and unstressed *quite*	Compound nouns from multi-part verbs Scale and limit words	Punctuation: colons and semicolons
	Word field: copy	Linking ideas: participle clauses
Stress in multi-part verbs	Suffixes Nouns into verbs	Referring back
Sentence stress	Word field: films Word formation	Referring back
	Family relations	Cohesion: additions and contrasts
The /əʊ/ sound	Colour words	Writing a summary
	Animal expressions	Ambiguity
Defining and non-defining relative clauses	Multi-part verbs Word field: the unusual	Defining and non-defining relative clauses: – punctuation – to link ideas
	Multi-part verbs: verb + adverbial particle + preposition	Cohesive ties
Multi-syllable word stress		Topic and comment sentences
	Collocation	Punctuation
	Idioms of comparison	Writing a summary
Intonation of question tags	The Media	Organising ideas

Down memory's lanes

▼

VOCABULARY

Memory

Underline the correct alternative in each of these sentences.

a) *Remind/remember* me to phone Adam.

b) Traditionally, children were made to *remember/memorise* poetry.

c) When he retired, he started to write his *memories/memoirs*.

d) This countryside *remembers/reminds* me of England.

e) The town decided to build a *memorial/memoir* in her honour.

f) I've got a terrible *mind/memory* for names.

g) Will you *remember/remind* to pick up the wine?

h) They stood in silence in *memorial/memory* of the dead.

i) Perhaps this music will *remember/remind* you.

j) This photo brings back old *memories/memoirs*.

LISTENING

1   [1.1] Before you listen to this interview with a psychologist try to match the terms with the examples.

a) episodic memory   1 how to change a lightbulb

b) factual memory   2 where you left your glasses

c) semantic memory   3 the taste of mangoes

d) skills memory   4 a friend's telephone number

e) sensory memory   5 road signs

Listen to the interview and check your answers.

2   Listen again and write *T* (for *True*) or *F* (for *False*).

a) People do not lose their semantic memory. ☐T☐

b) Traditional education encouraged the use of episodic memory. ☐

c) Learning vocabulary can involve both semantic and sensory memory. ☐

d) As you get older your factual memory suffers most. ☐

e) The ability to learn languages depends on episodic memory. ☐

3   Dictation. Listen to the interview again, and complete these sentences. (You may have to play the cassette several times.)

a) A lot of education – well traditionally anyway –

_____

_____ facts.

b) Even amnesiacs – people who lose their memory, so to speak – _____

_____ language.

c) Most adults are familiar with the sensation ____

_____

_____ recently.

d) We should be careful of confusing _____

_____

_____ ones.

READING

1 Read these two short extracts and decide which type of memory each one deals with. Choose from the words in the box.

| episodic factual semantic skills sensory |

A

> Opening a book of poetry
> That he hadn't looked at in ages,
> As if it were a bunch of flowers
> He sniffs the book's pages,
> And he recalls his youth again
> And his youth's rages.
>
> And all the intervening time disperses:
> A smell more redolent than any verses.

(by Byron H. Truscott)

B

> FATHER: Funny - seeing that photograph again - brought it all back.
> ALAN: Yes?
> FATHER: Those Saturday afternoons. My goodness it used to get cold sometimes.
> ALAN: It certainly did. [ALAN *sits back on his heels and looks at his* FATHER.] I could never understand ....
> FATHER: Other things?
> ALAN: Hmm?
> FATHER: Things we did together. Yesterday I was trying to remember ... Then I saw the photograph - and everything. ... We used to walk - d'you remember? - when you were quite small, we used to walk to the end of the road together?
> ALAN: Did we?
> FATHER: There was a small river. Quite a small river ....

(from *Talking to a Stranger* by John Hopkins)

2 Answer the following questions.

a) Find an expression in text A which means 'remembers'. _____

b) Find an expression in text B that means 'reminded me'. _____

TALKING EFFECTIVELY

Rhythm

[1.2] Listen to the recording and mark the main stressed syllables in each line of this poem.

I re<u>mem</u>ber, I re<u>mem</u>ber,
The house where I was born,
The little window where the sun
Came peeping in at morn;
He never came a wink too soon,
Nor brought too long a day,
But now I often wish the night
Had borne my breath away!

(from *I remember, I remember* by Thomas Hood)

Now practise saying the poem, keeping to the rhythm.

LEARNING GRAMMAR

Error correction

Identify and underline the errors in this student composition. Rewrite the correct version in your notebook.

The sunday night past, the doorbell rangs, I opened the door and I has got a big surprise, my brother was stoping in the door. He was changing a lot of, but he was having the same smile as always. He was more tall and more thin. He was having many hair but him looking was very interesting, my brother always was a goodlooking. Now, he's twenty five years, he's lawyer and he works in 'Jhons & Smiht Society'. We speaked all night and we remembered a lot of thinks.

Verbs

Choose the best form of the verb in brackets to complete this text.

I (1 *never forget*) <u>will never forget</u> the hut by the Blue Lake. It (2 *be*) _____ twenty-five years now, and I (3 *never be*) _____ back in all that time. But even now, on occasions, if, for example, I (4 *climb*) _____ with friends in these northern mountains, the memory of that southern lake and its little hut (5 *fill*) _____ my heart with longing.

Paul and I (6 *hike*) _____ for three or four days when we finally (7 *reach*) _____ it. We (8 *cross*) _____ at least two mountain passes, each of them knee-deep in snow. The Blue Lake Hut (9 *be*) _____ to be our last stop before crossing a third. Then we (10 *descend*) _____ into the valley that (11 *lead*) _____ us back to the township and to civilization. Meanwhile we (12 *plan*) _____ to spend at least one night at Blue Lake, maybe two, depending on how tired we (13 *feel*), _____ and how promising the weather (14 *look*) _____.

We (15 *reach*) _____ the hut in the late afternoon, after a long hike through the bush, battling upstream over boulders and through ravines, pausing to admire some spectacular cascades on the way. We (16 *emerge*) _____ into a clearing, and there it (17 *be*)_____. The guidebook (18 *lead*) _____ us to expect a blue lake, but nothing as blue as this. It (19 *be*) _____ the colour of richest lapis, except in the shade, where it (20 *turn*) _____ to darkest indigo. It (21 *snow*) _____ recently, and the banks of fresh snow on the lake's rim (22 *set*) _____ it off perfectly. We (23 *stand*) _____ speechless and open-mouthed. A deer, startled at our sudden arrival, (24 *bolt*) _____ into the beech grove that (25 *border*) _____ the opposite shore.

Nouns

Correct the underlined noun phrase errors in the following examples from students' writing. Rewrite the correct sentences in your notebook.

a) We didn't know <u>nobody</u> but we soon met <u>an interesting people</u>.

b) When its door opened <u>a beautiful blue-eyes girl</u>, my cousin as my mother told me later, welcomed me.

c) <u>All of people</u> know that Japanese culture and customs are different from <u>another country</u>.

d) That was a nice surprise because we hadn't seen <u>us</u> for five years when we went to <u>our mother house</u> for <u>his 60 birthday</u>.

e) I remembered Frank as the man who was always unusual in <u>our friend's group</u>.

f) Sometimes <u>dog</u> isn't <u>the best man's friend</u>.

g) I turned on the radio and heard <u>a very bad new</u>: Freddie Mercury had died.

h) In London I took <u>a two floor bus</u> and of course crossed the city in <u>the highest floor</u>.

i) I have chosen to describe Stephen Hawking, <u>a notorious scientist</u> of our century.

WRITING

Diagnosis

Write a short 250 word composition in your notebook, beginning 'I'll never forget . . .' and ending 'It was one of the . . . est days of my life.'

Cosmic bodies

VOCABULARY

Word formation: compound adjectives

When we say someone is *hardworking* we mean, of course, that the person works hard. And a *level-headed* person is someone who has got a level head.

1   Match the words in column A with the words in column B to make compound adjectives.

A	**B**
a) hard	1 hearted
b) broad	2 suffering
c) good	3 skinned
d) long	4 looking
e) smooth	5 minded
f) thick	6 talking
g) kind	7 working

2   Using the adjectives you created in Exercise 1, supply an appropriate synonym to complete these sentences.

a) Kim is extremely *hardworking*. (*diligent*)

b) Aquarians are supposed to be very _____. (*tolerant*)

c) Don't worry about him. He's rather _____. (*not sensitive to insults*)

d) You're not as _____ with a beard. (*handsome*)

e) She's one of the most _____ people I know. (*charitable*)

f) Their _____ children have had to put up with a lot. (*bearing troubles patiently*)

g) The _____ car salesman sold them a complete wreck of a car. (*clever with words*)

TALKING EFFECTIVELY

Word stress: compound adjectives

The stress in compound adjectives tends to vary, according to whether the adjective precedes or follows the noun it qualifies. For example:

The minister congratulated his <u>hard</u>working team.
He is not only bright but he's hard<u>working</u>.

[🔲 2.1] Mark the stressed syllable in these sentences, and then listen to check your answers.

a) I was looking for someone a little more level-headed.

b) Her long-suffering mother was not surprised by the news.

c) I suspect he's rather thick-skinned.

d) Smooth-talking Senator Lamb failed to persuade the voters.

e) A more kind-hearted person I do not know.

f) Her level-headed approach impressed me greatly.

g) This book is suitable only for the broad-minded reader.

h) The reader who is not broad-minded may be offended.

READING

I didn't recognize Eva Kay when she greeted us at the door, and for a moment I thought we'd turned up at the wrong place. The only thing she wore was a full-length, multi-coloured kaftan, and her hair was down, and out, and up. She'd darkened her eyes with kohl so she looked like a panda. Her feet were bare, the toenails painted alternately green or red.

What was she up to now with Dad? What was going on in her front room?

Eva had pushed back the furniture. The curtains were drawn. Four middle-aged men and four middle-aged women, all white, sat cross-legged on the floor, eating peanuts and drinking wine. There was some chanting music going on that reminded me of funerals.

Eva turned off the standard lamp. Over the one remaining light she draped a large diaphonous neckscarf, leaving the room illuminated only by a pink glow. Her movements had become balletic. One by one people fell silent. Eva smiled at everyone.

'So why don't we relax?' she said. They nodded their agreement.

Eva turned to my father and bowed to him, Japanese fashion. 'My good and deep friend Haroon here, he will show us the Way. The Path.'

I laughed to myself, remembering how Dad couldn't even find his way to Beckenham.

Dad sat down at the end of the room. Everyone looked keenly and expectantly at him; though the two men near me glanced at each other as if they wanted to laugh. Dad spoke slowly and with confidence. The nervousness he'd shown earlier appeared to have disappeared. He seemed to know he had their attention and that they'd do as he asked. I was sure he'd never done anything like this before. He was going to wing it.

'The things that are going to happen to you this evening are going to do you a lot of good. They may even change you a little, or make you want to change, in order to reach your full potential as human beings. But there is one thing you must not do. You must not resist. If you resist, it will be like driving a car with the handbrake on.'

He paused. Their eyes were on him.

'We'll do some floor work. Please sit with your legs apart.'

They parted their legs.

'Raise your arms.'

They raised their arms.

'Now, breathing out, stretch down to your right foot.'

After some basic yoga positions he had them lying on their backs. To his soft commands they were relaxing their fingers one by one, then their wrists, toes, ankles, foreheads, and, peculiarly, their ears.

(from *The Buddha of Suburbia* by Hanif Kureishi)

1   Read the extract from the story and find evidence in the text that suggests that:

a) Eva's appearance had changed.

_____

_____

b) Dad had a bad sense of direction.

_____

_____

c) Not everyone was convinced by Dad at first.

_____

_____

d) Dad had lacked confidence before the session.

_____

_____

2   Which picture best represents Eva Kay? ☐

A   B   C

3   'He was going to wing it.' From the context, tick the most likely meaning of this expression.

a) He was going to fly. ☐

b) He was going to flee. ☐

c) He was going to improvise. ☐

d) He was going to make a mess of it. ☐

4   Language focus. Tick the statement which is correct in each of these pairs.

a) i) I thought we would come to the wrong address. ☐

ii) I thought we had come to the wrong address. ☐

b) i) Eva put on a kaftan when she greeted us. ☐

  ii) Eva had put on a kaftan when she greeted us. ☐

c) i) The guests were sitting on the floor when we arrived. ☐

  ii) The guests sat on the floor when we arrived. ☐

d) i) Dad seemed to know they'd do as he asked.

  ii) Dad seemed to know they'd done as he asked. ☐

e) i) Having raised their arms, they parted their legs. ☐

  ii) Raising their arms, they parted their legs. ☐

LEARNING GRAMMAR

Continuous tenses

Tick the sentence which sounds more likely in each of these pairs.

a) i) Whenever I see Ted, he always plays his guitar. ☐

  ii) Whenever I see Ted, he's always playing his guitar. ☐

b) i) My next-door neighbour is forever popping over with the latest bit of gossip. ☐

  ii) My next-door neighbour forever pops over with the latest bit of gossip. ☐

c) i) He always clapped his hands once, to signal the start of the session. ☐

  ii) He was always clapping his hands once, to signal the start of the session. ☐

d) i) He's constantly talking about the war. ☐

  ii) He's talking constantly about the war. ☐

e) i) Whenever I phone, their number is busy. ☐

  ii) Whenever I am phoning, their number is busy. ☐

f) i) I forever phone, but they are busy. ☐

  ii) I'm forever phoning, but they are busy. ☐

g) i) The bus was always stopping at each town. ☐

  ii) The bus always stopped at each town. ☐

h) i) He's forever talking when he eats. ☐

  ii) He forever talks when he's eating. ☐

LANGUAGE PATTERNS

Reporting verbs

Study these verb patterns.

say

SUBJECT	VERB	(optional INDIRECT OBJECT)	*that* clause
She	said	to them	(*that*) they should keep the secret.

tell

a)

SUBJECT	VERB	DIRECT PERSON OBJECT	*that* clause
She	told	them	(*that*) they should keep the secret.

b)

SUBJECT	VERB	DIRECT PERSON OBJECT	*to* + infinitive
She	told	them	*to* keep the secret.

1 Look at the verbs in the box below and answer the questions.

> insist instruct emphasise warn
> reassure remind announce order

a) Which of the verbs can take the place of *say* in this sentence?

  She said that they should keep the secret.

_____

b) Which of the verbs can take the place of *tell* in this sentence?

  She told them that they should keep the secret.

_____

c) Which of the verbs can take the place of *tell* in this sentence?

  She told them to keep the secret.

_____

2 Convert the following examples of direct speech to reported speech, using the appropriate language patterns.

a) 'Be quiet,' he ordered.
   He ordered them to be quiet.

b) 'It won't hurt,' he reassured us.

   _____

c) 'It might be dangerous,' he warned.

   _____

d) 'Don't resist,' he reminded us.

   _____

e) 'The session has begun,' announced my father.

   _____

f) 'Women, raise your arms!' he ordered.

   _____

g) 'Eva, breathe out,' he instructed.

   _____

h) 'We will need to concentrate,' he emphasised to us.

   _____

i) 'Eva, relax!' Dad insisted.

   _____

WRITING

Sequencing devices

Look at this diagram of an exercise. Use the sequencing devices in the box to write a description of the exercise in your notebook.

| Before you start . . .   Now . . .   Next . . . |
| Having done that . . .   At the same time . . . |
| Then . . .   Finally . . .   And then . . . |

2
3
4
5

1

6
7

Magic moments

▼

LEARNING GRAMMAR

Would

Replace the following examples of *would* by *used to* or *was going to*. Which could be replaced by neither?

a) When we were young we would spend every summer at the beach. *used to*

b) I thought it would rain this afternoon.

_____

c) I would, of course, vote Conservative if I were in Taunton, except I won't be there.

_____

d) Pat had already cut down to seven a day, but would smoke as many as twenty if she went to a party.

_____

e) Major Parker said Mark would continue to run the estate.

_____

f) When I was on tour with the Hothouse Five we would do a gig, travel all night, and play music all the time.

_____

g) Sometimes I would give them food, because I was thinking that if my son was in the same position, I hope someone would do the same for him.

_____

h) If he never returns, I would not be greatly surprised.

_____

i) Edmund didn't know then that one day he would be the luckiest man in Swindon.

_____

Future in the past

Underline the correct form of the verb in each of these sentences.

a) The Queen (*would/was going to*) open the new hospital but it wasn't finished in time.

b) I had to take a taxi this morning because Barry (*was meeting/would meet*) me at 10.00.

c) Little did he know that she (*was having/would have*) the baby the next day.

d) The last I heard was that they (*were going to/would*) open a restaurant in Hamilton.

e) They (*were to/would*) finish painting the flat next weekend, but I doubt it very much.

f) The day would come when Murray (*was forgetting/would forget*) his promise.

g) In 1901 he (*was to write/was going to write*) his last and best loved opera.

h) When I last saw her, she (*was going to/would*) have a baby.

TALKING EFFECTIVELY

Would

[3.1] Decide in which of these sentences *would* must be stressed and underline it. Write *O* if stress is optional. Then listen to the recording to check.

a) I would advise you to see a doctor.

b) He would say that, wouldn't he?

c) The teacher in Room 10? That would be Mona.

d) We would go looking for crabs.

e) If they would stay up to after midnight, no wonder they are tired.

f) She said she would be a little late this morning.

g) I would ask you to be quiet during this part of the tour.

READING

1   Make a list of words you associate with the beach in your notebook.

2   Read the article and note how many of your words appear. Tick them.

Sea Songs.

Musician Paul Norton, whose latest album is *Under a Southern Sky*, spent the first three years of his life under the southern skies of the bayside suburb of Parkdale, in Melbourne.

"I remember going to the beach as a little boy with my parents ... buckets, spades and hats with pompoms round the edge, the sort they had on prams. Later I'd go looking for crabs with my dad, exploring rock pools. Mum would always sit on the beach - I don't remember her ever going into the water. I think she had a nasty experience once.

"I loved the sound and the smell of the surf. When I was older, we'd go and have fish and chips on the beach at Seaford.

"I liked the bay, too. I loved going out fishing in a boat on the bay with my dad. He always made a big deal of it; we'd take bags of food. It was a big adventure - we'd be up at five, grab plenty of whitebait and we wouldn't return until about two. We'd fish for flathead, take it home and cook it. If we hadn't caught anything, we'd just buy something on the way home and pretend we had."

The beach also became part of Norton's teenage culture, in a very Australian way - the attraction was more girls than surf. "My friends and I would pile into an old Holden and hoon around, calling out to girls, driving around yelling out the window - I don't recall it ever got me anywhere."

These days his swimming activities have been somewhat curtailed by pollution and a greater awareness of the damage the sun can cause.

"I don't sunbake, I get too bored. I can't sit still long enough. I'm not a board surfer but I like to bodysurf. I use sunscreens more than I used to. And I tend to wear hats more often. I like hats.

"I'm more aware of pollution, too. I never swim much in Sydney and I wouldn't swim at Bondi. Elsewhere, the beaches aren't too bad. When the band's playing up the coast, you can just walk out the door onto a beach. We've just been touring and I loved the beaches at Coffs Harbour, Byron Bay ... I love being in Queensland for the beaches."

Norton, who, these days, lives in Moonee Ponds with his wife, rock singer Wendy Stapleton, sees the sea as a potential source of inspiration; one of his dreams is to have a house overlooking the ocean. "I like walking along the beach at night, especially in winter - it's just fantastic for generating thoughts and ideas. I'd love to have that on tap rather than have to jump in a car to get there." ■

(from *HQ Magazine*)

3 Tick the correct answer to these questions, according to the article.

a) When he was young, Paul lived:
   i) in a Sydney suburb near the beach. ☐
   ii) in a Melbourne suburb far from the beach. ☐
   iii) in a Melbourne suburb near the beach. ☐

b) 'He always made a big deal of it' (line 18) means:
   i) he prepared for it carefully. ☐
   ii) he paid a lot of money for it. ☐
   iii) he looked forward to it a lot. ☐

c) '...and pretend we had' (line 25) means:
   i) and pretend we had bought it. ☐
   ii) and pretend we had it. ☐
   iii) and pretend we had caught it. ☐

d) 'I don't recall it ever got me anywhere' (line 31) means:
   i) I don't remember if the Holden ever went anywhere. ☐
   ii) I don't remember that we had any success with the girls. ☐
   iii) I don't remember that it affected me in any way. ☐

e) These days he:
   i) goes to the beach less often. ☐
   ii) doesn't go to the beach at all. ☐
   iii) goes to the beach as often as before, but doesn't enjoy it as much. ☐

f) Moonee Ponds is a suburb:
   i) near the beach. ☐
   ii) not near the beach. ☐
   iii) on the beach. ☐

4 Language focus. In the article, find two examples of *would* that do not mean *used to*.

1 _____

2 _____

LISTENING

[🎞 3.2] Listen to these people reminiscing about their holidays as children, and complete the chart below.

	Place	Activities	Food
1			
2			
3			
4			

VOCABULARY

Compound nouns

The words in the box below can all form compounds with *sun*. For example, *sunscreen, sunhat, sunglasses, suntan*.

   screen   hat   glasses   tan

In each of the following sets of words, think of one word that can combine with all four to form compound nouns.

a)	horse	b)	bottle
	gull		melon
_____	shell	_____	tower
	shore		hole

c)	screen	d)	castle
	shield		bag
_____	mill	_____	storm
	break		paper

e)	stroke	f)	water
_____	burn	_____	cellar
	shade		fish
	bathe		mine

LANGUAGE PATTERNS

Look at these two sentences from the article *Sea Songs*.

1 *I'd go looking for crabs with my dad.*
2 *We'd go and have fish and chips on the beach.*

go + *-ing* is used for activities, such as sports and pastimes, that often involve movement: it is one activity.

go and [+ verb] is used when you move somewhere to do something, and then you do it: it is two activities.

Choose the most suitable form of the verb: *go and* [+ verb] or *go* + *-ing* in each case.

a) On Saturdays I usually go (*shop*) _____ in the High Street.

b) Go (*see*) _____ if the post has arrived.

c) We used to go (*fish*) _____ when we were young.

d) Shall we go (*eat*) _____ something?

e) I think you should go (*do*) _____ your homework.

f) This winter we plan to go (*ski*) _____ in France.

g) Go (*ask*) _____ the policeman where the station is.

h) Let's go (*camp*) _____ in that field.

i) We usually go (*camp*) _____ in the summer.

WRITING

Sequencers in narrative

Read this text and underline the best time adverbials.

We got to the beach in good time: the sun was (*just/soon*) coming up. Wiremu was waiting for us. He had arrived (*earlier/previously*) and was getting the boat ready. It was a clear, crisp morning, and a slight mist hung over the water. Murray and I pulled off our backpacks and changed into our bathers. (*Simultaneously/ Meanwhile*) Moana collected some wood together and made a small fire. She filled a billy with water from the stream. (*Presently/Suddenly*) the water boiled and we warmed ourselves on sweet, hot tea. (*Then/Soon*) we loaded the fishing gear into the boat, piled in, and Wiremu, with one sharp tug, kindled the motor into life. We set out for the island.

(*Later/Next*), around noon, when we were anchored off the island and with at least a dozen kahawai in the bottom of the boat, Moana suggested a swim. Wiremu took the boat closer to the island. (*At the same time/In the meantime*) Moana swam alongside, cutting through the water like a porpoise. (*Subsequently/Finally*) we landed on the island and had lunch, tearing off lumps of homemade bread and sucking the fresh sea-eggs that Wiremu had collected (*beforehand/since*). (*Afterwards/Eventually*) we lay down on the warm sand under the spreading pohutukawas, and, for an hour or so, dozed.

billy	: a metal can used for cooking over a fire
kahawai	: a New Zealand fish
pohutukawa	: a New Zealand coastal tree

What language do you speak?

▼

The language of business

Alen Matic

Here is a firm prediction for the year ahead. The impossible English language will be massacred, struggled with, cursed and brutalised by more students next year than ever before. It is the *lingua franca* of business to an extent not imaginable even a decade ago. Three-quarters of the world's mail, telexes and cables are in English; English is the medium of 80% of all information stored in the world's computers; 45% of scientific publications are in English. And each of these figures is growing.

English is now the official language of a number of international companies. Unilever, Philips, Olivetti and France's Total require English of their middle and top level managers. IVECO, an Italian truck maker, and Cap Gemini Sogeti, one of Europe's largest soft-ware producers, both use English as their house language.

The EFTA organisation has English as its official language despite the fact that none of its six member countries uses it as a native language. The EC, by contrast, so complicates its affairs by using all nine official languages that 60% of its administrative budget goes on translation and interpretation, despite the fact that most of its staff speak English or French.

The teaching of English as a foreign language is a major (£1 billion) business in Britain; it is as large as that again in continental Europe and twice as large in both America and Asia. It is growing by 10% a year. Over 800m people now speak English worldwide - one-fifth of the world's population. By 2000 the number will have climbed to over one billion.

The first foreign language the Japanese learn is English. Every Japanese child who finishes secondary school will have had an average of eight years of English language instruction for a total of over 1,000 hours. There are over 700 English language training schools in Tokyo alone; as many as there are in all of England. A further 13,000 Japanese students undertake courses, many of which emphasise language as well as technical skills, in America. Managers in Japanese firms are sometimes promoted for their English rather than for their business skills. The shortage of Japanese managers able to speak other European languages is far greater; this is a major factor in luring Japanese firms to Britain rather than anywhere else in the EC.

(from *The Economist*)

READING

1 Read the text and write questions for these answers.

a)   80% *What proportion of information stored in the world's computers is in English?*

b) Three-quarters _____

_____

_____

c) 45% _____

_____

_____

d) 60% _____

_____

_____

e) £1 billion _____

_____

_____

f) Over 800m _____

_____

_____

g) Over one billion _____

_____

_____

h) Over 1,000 _____

_____

_____

i) 13,000 _____

_____

2   Tick the statements which reflect the writer's point of view.

a) Learners have difficulty learning English. ☐

b) The EC could save money on translation and interpretation. ☐

c) In Japan English is rated less highly than business skills. ☐

d) More Japanese speak English than other European languages: this is good for British business. ☐

Articles

1   Complete the text below with *the* or *Ø(zero article)*.

Do you speak _____ Japanese?

_____ help is on the horizon. _____ growth in _____ Japanese instruction around _____ world is far faster than _____ growth in _____ English. Between 1967 and 1984, _____ number of _____ foreigners studying _____ Japanese increased from 37,000 to almost 600,000. _____ Japanese Ministry of _____ Education predicts that _____ number of _____ foreigners studying in _____ Japan will increase four-fold by 2000 from _____ present 25,000. On _____ opposite edge of _____ Pacific rim, _____ number of _____ students learning _____ Japanese at _____ American colleges and universities increased by 45% to 23,500. Worldwide, 80% of _____ people learning _____ Japanese are Asian, however, and only take it up as a third language after _____ English.

2   Look at the use of *the* in this extract from the first reading text.

> *The* teaching of English as a foreign language is a major (£1 billion) business in Britain... . Over 800m people now speak English worldwide - one-fifth of *the* world's population. By 2000 *the* number will have climbed to over one billion.

Note that the first example of *the* refers forward in the text to answer the question 'Which teaching?': the teaching of English as a foreign language.

The second example refers outside the text, to our general knowledge, to answer the question 'Which world?': the world in which we all live, and of which there is only one.

The third example refers back in the text to something already mentioned, to answer the question 'Which number?': the number of people who speak English, i.e. 800m.

3   Which of the examples of *the* in the following text refer:

a) back in the text (to something already mentioned)?

b) forward in the text (i.e. it is defined by what follows)?

c) outside the text, (i.e. to the reader's knowledge of the world)?

[1]*The* Government's decision last month to suppress [2]*the* publication of 500 pages of materials designed to help teachers improve their pupils' knowledge of language has led to such a welter of confused comment that it has become hard for anyone outside [3]*the* argument to grasp what is going on.

[4]*The* reason for [5]*the* heated dispute is simple: few issues in education arouse so much prejudice, among both progressives and traditionalists, as that of [6]*the* teaching of English grammar.

Older people attended schools that regarded [7]*the* formal teaching of grammatical terms as a foundation for good writing. For many of them [8]*the* teacher's retreat from parsing sentences on [9]*the* blackboard (subject, verb, object, complement, adverb and so on) represented a retreat from rigorous standards.

There is little evidence to support [10]*the* notion that formal grammar teaching makes much difference to pupils who struggle to express themselves. Teachers abandoned it largely because their classroom experience showed that less adept pupils were bemused and frustrated by artificial and mechanical explanation of rules and terms.

Unfortunately, [11]*the* teachers' retreat led to many young people emerging from school without ever having learnt, in any structured way, how to analyse [12]*the* form of [13]*the* language they use.

(from *The Independent*)

1 C	2	3	4	5	6
7	8	9	10	11	12
13					

VOCABULARY

Idioms: *rule*

1   Look at the expressions in the box using *rule*. Use your dictionary to check the meanings of any of the expressions that you don't know.

> as a rule
> rulebook
> the exception that proves the rule
> rules and regulations
> to stretch/bend the rules
> to work to rule
> rule of thumb

2   Complete these sentences using the expressions from the box in Exercise 1. Change the verb tense if necessary.

a)   The _____ was that no word should enter the dictionary until it had been in use for five years.

b)   The _____ for importing a foreign car are so frustrating that it really isn't worth the effort.

c)   The customs officers were _____ and it took us ages to get over the frontier.

d)   If you go by the _____, the job will take far too long. I'll show you some short cuts.

e)   _____, I don't take sugar in my coffee, but this is so strong I think I'll have a little.

f)   We are not supposed to use the company car at the weekend, but I suggest we _____ a little.

g)   This sort of hot dry weather in autumn is _____ in England.

WRITING

Spelling rules

Here are two spelling rules. Look at the letter and correct any examples of incorrect spelling. Be careful! There are some 'exceptions that prove the rule'.

- I before E except after C
- Drop the final E when adding -ING

Dear Frieda,

Did you recieve my last letter? I've been hopeing you would write: I'm dieing to hear from you. I'm writing cheifly to tell you an unbeleivable peice of news: I finally acheived what I have been trying to do all year – I passed my driveing test! What a releif! A year ago, when I started takeing lessons, it seemed inconcievable that one day I would actually get it. Tonight I am celebrateing with some freinds: thier surprise is nearly as great as mine.

Well, that's my news. How are you? It's freezeing here – good weather for skiing, but I spend most of the time lieing in bed – as you know I am a beleiver in liesure!

Lots of love,

Sheila.

LANGUAGE PATTERNS

1 Convert these sentences from active to passive.

a) They saw him leave in a hurry.
   He was seen to leave in a hurry.

b) They have heard her speak favourably of the new grammar.
   She _____
   _____

c) They made me learn spelling rules by heart.
   I _____
   _____

d) They saw the pupils enjoying the lesson.
   The pupils _____
   _____

e) They say the new materials are easy to use.
   The new materials _____
   _____

f) They didn't make the students do homework.
   The students _____
   _____

g) They heard the learners speaking French fluently.
   The learners _____
   _____

2 The passive is often used to position the topic of a text at the head of a sentence:

The English Language

English is spoken by some 350 million people worldwide. It is also studied by many millions more as a second or foreign language.

Choose the best way of continuing the following short texts:

a) The Normans invaded England in 1066.
   i) Many French words were introduced into English by them.
   ii) They introduced many French words into English.

b) There are a lot of words of Indian origin in English.
   i) Many of these were introduced by India's colonial rulers.
   ii) India's colonial rulers introduced many of these.

c) Samuel Johnson (1709–84) was an English critic and lexicographer.
   i) In 1755, a _Dictionary of the English Language_ was written by him.
   ii) In 1755, he wrote a _Dictionary of the English Language._

d) _The English Pronouncing Dictionary_ was one of the first attempts to describe how English is actually spoken.
   i) It was written by Daniel Jones, a British linguist and scholar.
   ii) Daniel Jones, a British linguist and scholar, wrote it.

e) English spelling is notoriously irregular.
   i) George Bernard Shaw, among others, has promoted alphabets designed to reform it.
   ii) Alphabets designed to reform it have been promoted by George Bernard Shaw, among others.

TALKING EFFECTIVELY

Stress on nouns and verbs

Mark the stressed syllables on the highlighted words in these sentences.

a) PERFECT
   i) Practice makes perfect.
   ii) A few months in an English-speaking country should perfect your pronunciation.

b) DESERT
   i) The captain is the last to desert the ship.
   ii) The Sahara is the largest desert in the world.

c) REBEL
   i) Wat Tyler was England's most famous rebel.
   ii) Teenagers who rebel use clothes as a form of protest.

d) PRESENT
   i) You are required to present yourself for a medical examination at 10.30 on Tuesday .
   ii) I can't remember the last time she gave me a present.

e) EXPORT
   i) The fall in the value of the pound had a positive effect on the export market.
   ii) My neighbours breed snails and export them to France.

What a coincidence!

▼

LEARNING GRAMMAR

1 Underline the correct verb forms in this text.

> A few years ago a woman (*told/had told*) British Rail she (*had/had had*) a vision of a fatal crash in which a freight train, pulled by engine 47 216, (*was/had been*) involved. Two years later, a freight train (*was/had been*) involved in a fatal crash, the circumstances being precisely of the kind she (*described/had described*), except that the engine number (*was/had been*) 47 299.
>
> An observant train-spotter, however, (*noticed/had noticed*) earlier that the engine number (*was/had been*) changed. The engine (*was/had been*), in fact, the old 47 216. Apparently BR (*were/had been*) sufficiently unnerved by the vision to order the change.

(from *The Observer*)

2 Correct the tense mistakes in these authentic examples of student writing. Then, correct any other mistakes you can find. Rewrite the correct sentences in your notebook.

a) My mother said me that my boyfriend, Andrew, was having a accident and he stayed in the General Hospital.

b) When we arrived in my house and I opened the door others friends were inside yet. They had been prepared the party and I was surprising.

c) When we arrived, the train leaved the station and we stayed in three long hours until the next train arrived.

d) I realised that they fell in love.

e) I didn't realise it was so late and the underground didn't work yet.

f) The man had been destroying the planet during centuries.

g) In this afternoon my cousin was killed the cat of his mother because the cat was in the road and my cousin don't he looked.

LISTENING

[5.1] Read this 'Coincidence Questionnaire'. Then, listen to the recording of three people's personal experiences and decide which category of coincidence each one is.

Coincidence 1: _____

Coincidence 2: _____

Coincidence 3: _____

Coincidence Questionnaire

About your coincidence

We would like to have a better picture of the coincidences people experience. You can help by filling in this questionnaire and sending accounts of coincidences you have experienced, particularly those which you feel have been 'meaningful'.

Were any of the coincidences you experienced in one or more of the following categories?

a Clusters, or sequences, of related names, numbers or events.

b Spontaneous association (e.g. when a name comes to mind and you hear it on the radio or meet the person).

c Spontaneous perception (e.g. when you perceive or sense something happening at a distance).
  i) in space
  ii) in time

d 'Small world' (encounters with people in improbable circumstances).

e 'Hidden hand'
  i) problem solving
  ii) prayer answering
  iii) guardian angel
  iv) other

f 'Mind over matter' (e.g. clocks stop, pictures fall, as if influenced by some event)

g Recovery of lost property.

h Other.

VOCABULARY

Idioms: *chance*

1   Look at the expressions in the box using *chance*. Use your dictionary to check the meaning of any of the expressions you don't know.

> by chance
> to chance upon
> on the off chance (that)
> chances are (that)
> stand a good/fair chance
> to chance it

2   Complete these sentences using the expressions from the box in Exercise 1. Change the verb tense if necessary.

a) 'Don't you think we ought to book a table?'
'No, let's _____.'

b) _____ you've never tasted kiwi fruit wine. You'll be pleasantly surprised when you do.

c) This book _____ of being shortlisted for the Booker Prize.

d) We queued all night _____ we'd get seats for the Pavarotti concert.

e) This is a rare first edition that I _____ _____ in a second-hand book shop last week.

f) If _____ you should run into Paul, can you ask him to phone me?

LANGUAGE PATTERNS

Convert the direct speech into reported speech, using the verbs in the box.

> persuade   remind   require   warn

a) ALICE: Please come to the party, Gavin!
GAVIN: OK.
Alice persuaded Gavin to come to the party.

b) TERRY: Remember to take your bus pass, Tony.

_____

c) IMOGEN: Remember, children, that the last train leaves at 10.30.

_____

d) RACHEL: Believe me, Nigel, Lima *is* the capital of Chile.
NIGEL: I believe you!

_____

e) BOSS: Smith, you will have to work late on Friday.

_____

f) BASIL: Whatever you do, Sybil, don't mention the war.

_____

g) POLICE: Tourists! There are pickpockets operating in the area.

_____

h) CAPTAIN: Passengers should return to their seats and fasten their safety belts.

_____

i) ZOOKEEPER: Children – do not feed the animals!

_____

j) JIM: Please lend me £5, Martin!
MARTIN: Here you are.

_____

k) GUARD: All visitors must show their tickets.

_____

READING

A Guardian Angel?

The most striking examples of coincidences which suggest benevolent intervention are those which have saved people from injury or worse. In a letter to [Arthur] Koestler, Sir Alec Guinness related how while he was in a play in the West End, he would set two alarm clocks to ensure waking up early enough each Sunday morning to go to the 8 o'clock Mass at Westminster Cathedral before catching the 9.50 from Waterloo to Portsmouth, to get to his home in the country; and although he normally woke up even before they went off, one Sunday he slept through both of them.

Glancing at one of the clocks when he awoke, he thought it read 7.50, which left him just time to get to the cathedral. Only when the service was in progress, did he realise that it was the 9 o'clock Mass. No matter, he thought, he could get the 10.50 train.

But when he arrived at Waterloo it was to be told the 9.50 had been derailed. He had been accustomed to find a seat in the front coach. The front coach of the 9.50, he heard later, had toppled over. Its occupants, severely knocked about, had been taken to hospital.

As Koestler pointed out to him, it was not simply the sleeping through two alarms that was significant; if he had not misread the time, ...

(from *A Matter of Chance or Destiny* by Brian Inglis)

1   Read the text and write *T* (for *True*) or *F* (for *False*) next to these statements.

a) Guinness was in the habit of going to Mass on Sunday mornings. ☐

b) There is a Mass at 8.00 and a Mass at 9.00. ☐

c) There is a train to Portsmouth at 9.50 and one at 10.50. ☐

d) He usually caught the 10.50. ☐

e) One Sunday morning he decided not to go to Mass but to go to Portsmouth instead. ☐

f) He set two alarm clocks, one for 8 o'clock and one for 9.50. ☐

g) On this particular Sunday he didn't hear the alarm clocks. ☐

h) He thought he had only ten minutes to get to the Mass. ☐

i) He realised it was 9 o'clock so he went straight to the station. ☐

j) He was on the 9.50 train when it was derailed. ☐

2   Tick which you think is the best ending to the story.

a) . . . he wouldn't have been late for Mass and would have caught the 9.50. ☐

b) . . . he would have been late for Mass and would have caught the 10.50. ☐

c) . . . he might have decided not to go to Mass in order to catch the 9.50. ☐

d) . . . he might have decided not to catch the 9.50 in order to go to Mass. ☐

TALKING EFFECTIVELY

Quiz

1   Answer these questions. The answers all have the sound /ɪ/ in them.

a) Helsinki is the capital of which country? *Finland*.

b) How many eggs in half a dozen? _____

c) What is the metal whose chemical sign is Sn? _____

d) What do you use for removing the lumps from flour? _____

e) What is the familiar form of the name William? _____

f) What was Dame Janet Baker famous for? _____

g) Who wrote *Leaves of Grass*? _____

h) What is a baby cat called? _____

i) What do the British eat with fish? _____

j) What did Cinderella lose? _____

2   [🖻 5.2] Look at these sentences and underline all examples of the sound /aɪ/. Then listen to the recording to check.

a) It's nine years since Lennon died.

b) I saw the Jackson Five live at the Isle of Wight.

c) Have you heard Prince's *Sign of the Times*?

d) *It's a long and windy road* had been revived by Bryan Ferry.

e) Miles Davis plays *A walk on the wild side*.

f) What was the title of the Beatles' *White* album?

g) And now, the *Minute Waltz*, played on the xylophone.

WRITING

Sequencers

Put the sequencers from the box into the following text, where appropriate.

immediately   whereupon (x 2)   earlier once   no sooner   meanwhile   later

_____, my wife was driving home through Kansas, where, _____, she had been visiting her mother in Kansas City. _____ had she left the city than she happened to see what looked like a microwave oven beside the road, _____ she stopped the car and got out. It was in perfectly good condition and, thinking that someone must have abandoned it, she heaved it into the backseat of the car. _____, nearing home, she happened to exceed the speed limit and, _____, she was stopped by a police car. She tried to talk her way out of it, but, _____ the policeman had noticed the 'microwave' in the backseat. It turned out that it was not a microwave at all, but a radar speed-checking device, _____ she was charged with theft as well as speeding

Susan's story

▼

VOCABULARY

Word formation: compound nouns derived from multi-part verbs

1 Match the words in column A with the words in column B to form compound nouns. (Some verbs can combine with more than one particle.)

A	B
a) mess	1 out
b) draw	2 over
c) turn (x3)	3 down
d) shut	4 -up
e) run (x2)	5 back
f) work	

2 Now, complete these sentences using the compound nouns from Exercise 1.

a) There was a terrible *mess-up* over the examination results because the teacher lost all the papers.

b) The _____ of the Ford factory caused the loss of four thousand jobs.

c) I like to have a good long _____ at the gym at least once a week.

d) I love skiing but it has one _____: its cost.

e) The company's _____ for the last financial year exceeded £12m.

f) The three candidates campaigned fiercely in the _____ to the election.

3 Choose combinations from the two columns to complete the sentences below. This time, the particle comes first. There are several possible combinations.

A	B
a) in	1 turn
b) on	2 take
c) out	3 put
d) up	4 set

a) The school's *intake* of new students for this year was 10% down on last year.

b) Sri Lanka's defeat of England in the cricket test was quite an _____ for the English supporters.

c) From the very _____, things started going wrong. For a start, Adrian had forgotten his passport . . .

d) After several disappointing years, the tourist industry is experiencing a welcome _____.

e) Her _____ is phenomenal: at least one novel a year for the last twenty five years.

f) The _____ of the disease is marked by chest pains and a bad cough. This is followed by a sore throat and high temperature.

g) His lectures are interesting but too dense: there's so much new _____ it gives you a headache.

h) I offered him the chance of a lifetime – job, car, furnished flat. But he was a bit slow on the _____. However, finally he accepted.

Scale and limit words

Complete the text below with *absolutely* or *extremely.*

It was an _____ freezing day when we arrived in Berlin, and I was _____ unhappy, as I hadn't bothered to pack warm clothes. We were taken to Potsdam on the first day, and although the palace was _____ interesting, we had an _____ disgusting meal, compounded by the fact that the waiter was _____ rude. The only consolation was that it was _____ cheap. Nevertheless, we were both in an _____ bad mood by the time we got back to the city. The following day was _____ marvellous. Because it was still _____ cold, we decided to do the museums, my favourite being the Antiquities Museum with the bust of Nefertiti: an _____ beautiful piece, although I was _____ surprised to discover that she has one eye missing.

TALKING EFFECTIVELY

Quite

[📼 6.1] When *quite* is stressed it can mean 'only a little' or 'not as much as expected'. It can therefore convey a negative opinion. For example:

The play was quite good. = Not very good.
The play was quite good. = Good, although not very good.

Listen to the recording and, in each case, decide if the opinion is positive (*P*) or negative (*N*).

a) The weather was quite good. ☐
b) The weather was quite good. ☐
c) The people were quite friendly. ☐
d) Martina played quite well. ☐
e) Her husband is quite attractive. ☐
f) Your essays are quite well-written. ☐
g) The article was quite interesting. ☐
h) The article was quite interesting. ☐

LEARNING GRAMMAR

Adverb order

1 Complete these sentences by putting the words in the correct order.

a) judge / comes / the
Here *comes the judge*.

b) well / plays / tennis
She _____

c) I / do / the / do / housework
Seldom _____

d) up / came / firemen
_____ the _____

e) often / the / don't / to / I / go
_____ cinema.

f) he / mouth / open / rarely / his
_____ does _____

g) understand / she / only / did
_____ then _____

h) bus / corner / the / the / came
Around _____

i) so / I / eaten / well / have
Never _____

2 Complete this children's rhyme with the words in the box.

out (×2) away up down

Incey Wincey Spider
Climbing _____ the spout.
_____ came the rain
And washed poor Incey _____.
_____ came the sun
_____ went all the rain.
Incey Wincey Spider
Climbed the spout again.

Adjective order

Choose the best word in brackets to complete these sentences.

a) She gave me an _unusual_ little Chinese ornament.

   (antique/unusual/ivory)

b) It was made of tiny green _____ beads.
   (beautiful/plastic/round)

c) I'm looking for a plain _____ ceramic pot.
   (functional/flower/white)

d) Have you seen a blue plastic _____ pen?
   (small/ball-point/new)

e) She was wearing an attractive navy blue _____ fisherman's pullover.
   (second-hand/bulky/woollen)

f) They live in a run-down thirties _____ cottage.
   (beach/cream-coloured/little)

g) Try it with a dry white _____ table wine.
   (chilled/Californian/nice)

READING

1   Read the text opposite and write *F* (for *False*) against the appropriate statements.

a) She can't understand what the nurses say because she can't hear them. ☐

b) She thinks there is no coffee because she can't see it. ☐

c) She has lost the idea of 'left' because the right-hand side of her brain was damaged. ☐

d) She finds it easier to rotate her plate than rotate herself. ☐

Eyes Right!

Mrs S., an intelligent woman in her sixties, has suffered a massive stroke, affecting the deeper and back portions of her right cerebral hemisphere.

She sometimes complains to the nurses that they have not put dessert or coffee on her tray. When they say, "But, Mrs S., it is right there, on the left," she seems not to understand what they say, and does not look to the left. If her head is gently turned, so that the dessert comes into sight, in the preserved right half of her visual field, she says, "Oh, there it is – it wasn't there before." She has totally lost the idea of "left", both with regard to the world and her own body. Sometimes she complains that her portions are too small, but this is because she only eats from the right half of her plate. Sometimes, she will put on lipstick, and make up the right half of her face, leaving the left half completely neglected: it is almost impossible to treat these things, because her attention cannot be drawn to them and she has no conception that they are wrong. She knows it intellectually, and can understand, and laugh; but it is impossible for her to know it directly.

Knowing it intellectually, she has worked out strategies for dealing with her imperfection. She cannot look left, directly, she cannot turn left, so what she does is to turn right – and right through a circle. And now if she cannot find something which she knows should be there, she swivels to the right, through a circle, until it comes into view. She finds this signally successful if she cannot find her coffee or dessert.

It would seem far simpler for her to rotate the plate than rotate herself. But it is oddly difficult, it does not come naturally, whereas whizzing round in her chair does, because her looking, her attention, her spontaneous movements and impulses, are all now exclusively and instinctively to the right.

(from *The Man Who Mistook His Wife for a Hat* by Oliver Sacks)

2   The following sentences have been taken out of the text. Put them back in by marking the text a, b, c, d at the appropriate point.

a) She has perfectly preserved intelligence – and humour.

b) It does not occur to her that it has a left half as well.

c) Thus she requested, and was given, a rotating wheelchair.

d) She agrees, and has tried this – or at least tried to try it.

LANGUAGE PATTERNS

Clause negation

She seems not to understand . . . This means the same as *She doesn't seem to understand.* In this case, it makes no difference to the meaning which verb is negated, *seem* or *understand*, although *She seems not to understand* is a more formal, literary construction. Another construction – *She seems to not understand. . .* – is avoided by purists as it contains a split infinitive. However, it is perfectly acceptable in informal speech.

There are other verbs, however, where the position of the negative does affect the meaning:

She didn't try to look. and *She tried not to look.* are very different in meaning.

Convert these sentences into the alternative negative form, and then decide if the meaning is the same(*S*) or different(*D*).

a) She offered not to go.
   She didn't offer to go. [D]
b) They didn't appear to be enjoying themselves.

   _____ □

c) Samuel agreed not to speak.

   _____ □

d) It doesn't tend to rain much in spring.

   _____ □

e) I didn't expect to recognise you.

   _____ □

f) He managed not to do the dishes.

   _____ □

g) I don't intend to talk to him, if I can help it.

   _____

   _____ □

h) He pretended not to laugh.

   _____ □

i) The government promised not to raise the interest rate.

   _____

   _____ □

j) I don't wish to be disturbed.

   _____ □

WRITING

Punctuation: colons and semicolons

The colon (:) is generally used to show that what follows is an explanation, or an example, of what precedes the colon. It is also used to introduce lists.

The semi-colon (;) is used to separate two sentences that are closely linked in meaning.

Connect these sentences using either a colon or a semi-colon at the point marked |.

a) There are a number of brain diseases associated with old age | Alzheimer's and Parkinson's are just two of the more well-known.
b) The risk of developing Alzheimer's increases sharply over the age of 65 | the risk of developing Parkinson's is also high.
c) But brain disorders are not confined to the old | strokes can afflict people as young as forty.
d) On top of this comes a new threat to the young | HIV, which can infect brain cells and cause dementia.
e) Detection of brain disorders is difficult and costly | treatment is even more so.
f) Psychological tests and brain scans can help detect disorders | ultimately a postmortem is the only way of confirming the disease.
g) There are also moral issues at stake | the use of foetal tissue and the use of animals for experimental purposes, for example.

Believe it or not . . .

▼

VOCABULARY

1   The words at the top of the tables (all nouns) are used to refer to things that are not original. These things can be legal or illegal (Table 1). The words are generally associated with different types of things (Table 2). Tick the two tables according to the associations each word has (some words have more than one association).

Table 1	copy	facsimile	replica	imitation	fake	counterfeit	forgery
both legal and illegal	✓						
usually legal							
usually illegal							

Table 2	copy	facsimile	replica	imitation	fake	counterfeit	forgery
things in general	✓						
money							
paintings	✓						
documents	✓						
3-dimensional objects							
signatures	✓						
textiles/ fabrics	✓						

2   Write down the verbs for these nouns.

copy *to copy*

imitation _____

facsimile _____

fake _____

replica _____

counterfeit _____

forgery _____

3   Select words from Exercises 1 or 2 to complete these sentences.

a) His attempt to _____ my signature didn't fool the bank.

b) The firm gave me a briefcase. Unfortunately it was made of _____ leather.

c) The British Museum is publishing a _____ edition of *Captain Cook's Voyages*.

d) Could I make a _____ of this article?

e) He was arrested for handling _____ banknotes.

f) After a long investigation, they concluded that the painting was a _____.

g) They are collecting money to build a _____ of Captain Cook's ship, *The Endeavour*.

LISTENING

Shopping in Hong Kong

1 [📼 7.1] Listen to the recording and match the shopping items in column A with the places in Hong Kong in column B.

A	**B**
a) discount cassettes	1 Factory outlets
b) Chinese cashmere sweaters	2 Stanley Market
c) lacquerware	3 Jade Market
d) jade items	
e) 'seconds'	4 Night Markets
f) cheap silks	
g) fake Samsonite suitcases	5 The laneways
h) Tiger Balm ointment	6 Western Market
i) imitation Hermes scarves	7 China Product stores
j) copy designer watches	
k) copy Chanel handbags	
l) hand-crafted stationery	

2 Listen to the conversation again, and mark the places in column B on the map of Hong Kong.

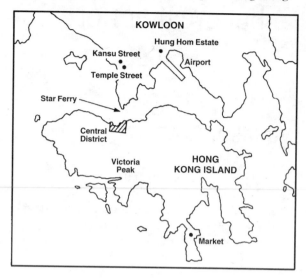

LEARNING GRAMMAR

Adverbial participle clauses

1 Rewrite these sentences using the prompts.

a) Being Canadian, she had to have a visa.
   Since she was Canadian, she had to have a visa.

b) Not having an alarm clock, he overslept.
   As _____

c) Having found somewhere to park, they were able to take their time.
   Once _____
   _____

d) Having decided on the film, we'd better think of a restaurant.
   Now that _____
   _____

e) Ignored by their parents, children grow anxious.
   If _____
   _____

f) Having lost the keys, he had to break down the door.
   Since _____
   _____

g) Simon being married, Helen settled for David.
   Seeing that _____
   _____

2   Rewrite these sentences using participle clauses.

a) Since I hadn't brought an umbrella, I got soaked.
    Not having brought an umbrella, I got soaked.

b) Once he'd practised a few times, he got very good at it.

_____

_____

c) Now that you've been overseas, you ought to settle down.

_____

_____

d) Since the doctor had said nothing, she felt less worried.

_____

_____

e) Seeing that it was a Sunday, she slept in.

_____

_____

f) If it's given a coat of paint, it will look like new.

_____

_____

g) As you are our local MP, you might like to get involved.

_____

_____

3   Rewrite these sentences so as to remove their ambiguity.

a) Being a Doberman, I decided to keep my distance.
    It being a Doberman, I decided to keep my distance.
    As it was a Doberman, I decided to keep my distance.

b) Having been freshly renovated, she decided to buy the house.

_____

_____

c) Stripped and cleaned, we realised that the painting was a genuine masterpiece.

_____

_____

d) Being cold and rainy, I decided to stay in.

_____

_____

e) Having been in the cellar for nearly a century, our host announced that it was time to drink the burgundy.

_____

_____

f) Being the first book she had published, I read it with some interest.

_____

_____

g) Filmed in black and white, the audience soon lost interest in the movie.

_____

_____

h) Considered by critics to be a work of genius, we were looking forward to seeing it.

_____

_____

i) Marinated in wine and fresh herbs, his wife served the lamb.

_____

_____

4   Participle clauses are often used to set the scene by providing background information. Here are the opening lines of six poems. Can you match the first line (in column A) with the second line (in column B) of each poem?

A	B
a) Riding at dawn, riding alone,	1 I watch the door as it slowly opens -
b) Having eliminated his dear brother	2 At first we failed to find the grave
c) Walking among the oaks and snails and mossed inscriptions	3 The moon is staggering in the sky;
d) Looking by chance in at the open window	4 Gillespie left the town behind;
e) Drowsing in my chair of disbelief	5 He let tears fall and wandered off alone
f) Crazed through much child-bearing	6 I saw my own self seated in his chair

LANGUAGE PATTERNS

1   In the following pairs of sentences, identify those with the same or similar meaning (*S*), and those with different meaning (*D*):

a) We stopped to discuss the results of the tests.
    We stopped discussing the results of the tests. ☐ *D*

b) I hate to have to interrupt your dinner.
    I hate having to interrupt your dinner. ☐

c) When did they start going out together?
    When did they start to go out together? ☐

d) I tried turning the water off at the mains.
    I tried to turn the water off at the mains. ☐

e) He said that he remembered leaving the keys under the mat.
    He said that he remembered to leave the keys under the mat. ☐

f) I prefer to take a shower before breakfast, not after.
    I prefer taking a shower before breakfast, not after. ☐

2   Underline the correct form of the verb to complete the passage.

. . . It had stopped (*to rain/raining*). Grace gathered her things and stepped outside. The air was fresh and bracing as she set out towards the village. Her mind was made up. She would throw herself on the mercy of the villagers. She remembered (*to read/reading*) somewhere that every village in the valley had its own local sorceress. . . She cut across the turnip field and attempted (*climbing/ to climb*) the fence, but the rain had left it wet and slippery. She regretted not (*having/to have*) put on her walking shoes. Working her way along the fence, trying (*to avoid/avoiding*) the puddles that had formed in the furrows, she let herself be guided by the lights of the village, and remembered, just in time, (*leaping/to leap*) the stream that carried the pigswill down into the lake. The village square

was deserted and she stopped (*to consider/ considering*) her next step. Then, with a burst of resolve, she thrust herself into the bar, where Herr Bachmann, startled and alone, stared at her through a haze of cigar smoke, arrested in the act of polishing the bar.

   'I regret (*to inform/informing*) you that we are closed,' he said coldly, and went on (*to clean/ cleaning*) the bar . . .

(by *Ruth Norby*)

WRITING

Participle clauses

Participle clauses can be used to link ideas. For example:

We arrived home. We were tired but happy. = *Tired but happy, we arrived home.*
I hadn't seen the red light. So I didn't stop. = *Not having seen the red light, I didn't stop.*

Rewrite the following passage in your notebook, connecting the sentences in square brackets by using participle clauses.

[I hadn't flown into Hong Kong before. So I was unprepared for the sudden steep descent to the airport.] [I was visibly shaking. I was clutching the armrests. I watched the tenement buildings flashing by.] You could practically reach out and touch the washing that hung from the balconies. [My neighbour noticed my terror. He leant over and said: 'This is nothing compared to taking-off!'] [I remembered that I was booked to fly on to Beijing later that same evening. So I didn't thank him for this observation.] The plane touched down without so much as a bump. [I was embarrassed by my display of nerves. But I was relieved that we had at least landed safely. I disembarked. I was looking forward to my few hours' stopover in Hong Kong.]

Fame and fortune

▼

READING

1 Read the article and then number the following stages of Anne Summers' life in chronological order.

journalist ☐   businesswoman ☐
academic ☐   editor ☐   bureaucrat ☐

New York Summers

ANNE SUMMERS IS IN LOVE - WITH NEW YORK, with life, and with a younger man. The woman who gave us one of the groundbreaking manifestos of Australian feminism, *Damned Whores and God's Police*, whom Bob Hawke appointed to head the nascent Office for the Status of Women, and who went on to edit - and co-own - the American feminist magazine *Ms*, is now enjoying a stylish Manhattan lifestyle, and making no apologies for it.

These days, home for Summers is a two-storey apartment on Manhattan's Upper West Side, in a classy building complete with doorman. Around the corner are the speciality food stores where she likes to shop - "sometimes twice a day, like a French housewife" - returning home to cook meals for guests or for the man in her life, Chip, a Texan who works in advertising.

"I get an incredible thrill out of living here," she says. "There are certain things about New York that I don't like but I do like the fact that it encourages you to strive harder, to break new barriers. Americans worship success and if you are successful, they will forgive you practically anything. At the same time they will allow you to re-invent yourself. A lot of Australians try to paint what happened at *Ms* as a failure, but in America they say, 'OK, what is she going to do next?' You'd have to have a series of disasters before they'd write you off."

All this is a long way from Adelaide, where Summers grew up, the eldest of six children in a Catholic working-class family. And it is a long way, too, from her days as a radical feminist, from the "angry young woman" who wrote *Damned Whores* and who established *Elsie*, Sydney's first women's refuge.

The road from Adelaide to Manhattan has been eventful and has required a number of metamorphoses: from rebellious teenager to radical feminist to mainstream journalist to feminist bureaucrat or "femocrat" to high-powered New York businesswoman. It has been an exciting journey but it has also, at times, been rocky. Very rocky. ...

When she was 16, Summers was taken by her aunt to Fanny's restaurant in Melbourne. "It was the most glamorous place I had ever been," she says. And it was an eye-opener. So was her aunt, who was one of the few single professional women she had ever met. "I thought she was incredibly glamorous because she worked in a bank. It probably wasn't a very glamorous job at all, but it seemed so to me."

Her aunt and her Catholic education were two of the strongest influences in Summers' life - the former showed her that there was an alternative life to that of housewife and mother, and the latter gave her a social conscience.

Whatever else may have changed about Summers, her sense of justice is as strong as ever. When she went to university she began to concentrate her attention on the injustices suffered by women. She took up women's rights both as an academic and an activist. After entering journalism comparatively late (she was 30), she made a rapid rise through the ranks to become political correspondent for *The Australian Financial Review*. From there, in 1983, she was chosen by the new Prime Minister, Bob Hawke, to head the Office for the Status of Women. She became a "femocrat" and probably the most influential woman in Australia.

Summers is essentially a pragmatist. "I think I'm still an idealist but I keep coming back to the fact that it is better to have 50 per cent of what you want than 100 per cent of nothing. If you've got the means of getting something done, use it. It is very important that women have access to power, either by occupying it or by having access to people who occupy it."

So what's next? "I guess now I am in a period of transition. I'm trying to figure out if I want to get back to full-time writing or get involved in some other kind of venture."

In the meantime, she will continue to live - and love - in New York. ▪

(from *HQ Magazine*)

2 Write *T* (for *True*) or *F* (for *False*) next to these statements, according to the article.

a) Summers is currently editor of *Ms.* ☐

b) It was her mother who gave her a social conscience. ☐

c) Among other things, she has been a full-time writer. ☐

d) What happened at *Ms* was considered a failure by many Australians. ☐

e) Americans are more forgiving than Australians. ☐

f) She is not ashamed of her present life-style. ☐

g) She believes you shouldn't compromise your ideals. ☐

3 Vocabulary. Circle the word or phrase in each group which is most different in meaning from the others.

a) influential, ground-breaking, high-powered, successful

b) rebellious, radical, angry, mainstream

c) rocky, stylish, classy, glamorous

d) write off, failure, transition, disaster

e) strive, break barriers, rise through the ranks, re-invent oneself

VOCABULARY

Suffixes

1 Look at the words in the box from the article *New York Summers* and write down the abstract nouns from which these agent nouns are derived. Which is the odd one out and why?

feminist journalist activist idealist pragmatist

2 Find *-ist* words for the following definitions. Which of them have an associated abstract noun?

a) A person travelling on vacation.
Tourist - Tourism

b) A medical practitioner specialising in teeth.

_____

c) A person who faces facts; not a dreamer.

_____

d) A person who rides a bicycle.

_____

e) A person who writes in order to make people laugh.

_____

f) A person who believes that their sex is better than the other sex.

_____

g) A person who studies animals.

_____

h) A person who sells flowers.

_____

i) A person who believes in peace, not war.

_____

j) A person who plays the flute.

_____

Nouns into verbs

She was chosen by the new Prime Minister, Bob Hawke, to head the Office for the Status of Women.

Complete the following text, using verbs derived from the parts of the body marked on the drawing.

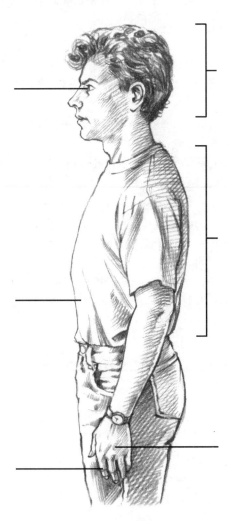

'As a senior police officer,' O'Connor told the assembled officers, 'I have been chosen to _____ the new Animal Violence Task Force. I'm counting on your support, and I need three officers to _____ me on this. It's a tough job, and if you can't _____ violence, don't apply. Right, any volunteers?' he said, _____ Officer Lenaghan. 'Lenaghan, are you man enough?' Lenaghan hung his head, and _____ his badge. 'I'm sorry, sir,' he said, finally. 'I can't do it. Here – take this.' He _____ O'Connor his badge, turned on his heel, and _____ for the door.

LEARNING GRAMMAR

Future continuous

The future continuous is often used to introduce requests. For example:

A: *Will you be using your computer this afternoon?*
B: *No. Why?*
A: *Do you think I could borrow it?*

Write similar request-introductions using the prompts in A. Then match the request-introductions with the requests in B below.

A

a) use/computer/this afternoon?
   Will you be using your computer this afternoon? 4

b) need/car/tomorrow?
   _____ ☐

c) want/butter/immediately?
   _____ ☐

d) go/supermarket/this morning?
   _____
   _____ ☐

e) wear/pearl earrings/tonight?
   _____
   _____ ☐

f) pass/post office/this afternoon?
   _____
   _____ ☐

g) see/Maria/on Monday?
   _____ ☐

B

1 Do you think I could borrow them?
2 Could you ask her to phone me?
3 Could you get me some stamps?
4 Do you think I could borrow it?
5 Could you get me some cat food?
6 Do you think I could borrow some?
7 Do you think I could borrow it?

LANGUAGE PATTERNS

Multi-part verbs: transitive multi-part verbs

She took up women's rights ...
You'd have to have a series of disasters before they'd write you off.

Take up and *write off* are both transitive verbs, i.e. they take objects. They are formed from a verb and an adverb particle. Note that the first two parts of these kind of multi-part verbs are always separated if the object is a pronoun: *they'd write you off*, not *they'd write off you*.
Otherwise, the adverb particle can go either before or after the object, except in cases where the object is rather long:

He wrote the car off.
He wrote off the car.
He wrote off the car he had borrowed that evening from his brother.

1   In the following sentences, place the adverb particle where it fits best. (In some cases, it may fit in more than one position.)

a) I know some people who will put you *up* for the night. (*up*)
b) We have been asked to sort the problem of the exam papers that were thrown away. (*out*)
c) She told the children for smoking. (*off*)
d) The police are trying to track the woman, her two accomplices, and the driver of the van. (*down*)
e) Ann Summers can't figure what to do with her life. (*out*)
f) If we can't afford a party, let's call it. (*off*)
g) This vote could bring the government. (*down*)
h) Why don't you talk it with your flatmate? (*over*)
i) I can't spin this exercise much longer. (*out*)

2   Match the following verbs with the multi-part verbs in Exercise 1.

cancel $\boxed{f}$ resolve ☐   extend ☐   discuss ☐
accommodate ☐   defeat ☐   decide ☐
reprimand ☐   locate ☐

Adverbs and prepositions

Multi-part verbs that consist of verb + preposition always have objects. The object always follows the preposition, even when the object is a pronoun. Exceptions:
• when the object is a question word like *What, Who,* etc.: *Who is he living with?*
• in relative clauses: *Is it Kim who he's living with?*

1   In these sentences, which of the underlined words are adverbs (*A*), and which are prepositions (*P*)?

a) I wonder if you could look <u>after</u> the plants while we're away? ☐
b) Isn't it time we did the reception <u>up</u>? ☐
c) Who shall we drink <u>to</u>? ☐
d) David? We ran <u>across</u> him in Suez. ☐
e) Harry? We ran him <u>down</u> in Luxor. ☐
f) Edward? Isn't he the chap we ran <u>into</u> in Aswan? ☐
g) Nothing will wipe <u>out</u> the memory of that summer. ☐
h) Can I try <u>on</u> this pullover? ☐
i) They turned <u>down</u> the applicant for the job. ☐
j) They turned <u>down</u> the second street on the left. ☐

2   Match the verb + adverb combinations in Exercise 1 with these verbs or expressions.

erase ☐   refuse ☐   to put it on to see if it fits ☐
decorate ☐   chase and catch ☐

TALKING EFFECTIVELY

Multi-part verbs: stress on adverbs and prepositions

[▭ 8.1] Listen to the recording and mark the stressed word in each question. Which words are stressed – adverbs or prepositions?

a) Which applicant did they turn down?
b) Which street did you turn down?
c) You're going visiting? Who are you going to call on?

d) You want to use the phone? Who are you going to call up?

e) What bridge did the cars pass on?

f) What news did the doctor pass on?

g) What door did you knock on?

h) Which boxer did you knock out?

WRITING

Referring back

'Her aunt and her Catholic education were two of the strongest influences in Summers' life – *the former* showed her that there was an alternative life to that of housewife and mother, and *the latter* gave her a social conscience.'

1 Rewrite the following, using *the former* and/or *the latter*.

a) I studied Latin and Greek. Latin taught me how to think. Greek taught me how to feel.

_____

_____

_____

b) We visited Naples and Florence. We were seduced by food in Naples, and by art in Florence.

_____

_____

_____

c) It was in Simla that we met Tusker and his wife. I didn't think much of his wife.

_____

_____

_____

d) Foreign travel is nothing compared to the pleasure of reading good books. I would happily forego foreign travel if I could spend my life reading good books.

_____

_____

_____

e) I have already written to you about the possibility of your opening the exhibition as well as writing an introduction to the catalogue. With regard to your opening the exhibition, there is already a great deal of interest.

_____

_____

_____

_____

_____

2 Other ways of referring back in the text. Complete the letter below using the expressions in the box.

previous above thus in this way there then enclosed the latter this

3 What is being referred to, in each case, in the letter?

1 _____   6 _____

2 _____   7 _____

3 _____   8 _____

4 _____   9 _____

5 _____

CTEFLA Course 11th
January - 4th February

I am pleased to be able to offer you a place on the ¹_____ course, pending receipt of a deposit of £100, as outlined in the ²_____ fees information. It's best to send ³_____ by means of a bank transfer, ⁴_____ avoiding problems with the post. As I mentioned in a ⁵_____ letter, there will be a pre-course orientation meeting on Friday 8th January at 2.00 p.m., at the Institute. The best way to get ⁶_____ is to take either the underground or a No 45 bus. ⁷_____ will drop you right outside the Institute. The meeting will finish at 4.00, and usually course participants ⁸_____ go for a drink. ⁹_____ you will have a chance to meet your colleagues informally.

The film or the book?

▼

VOCABULARY

1 Complete the chart below by putting the words in the box into four 'families' of three words each.

> cast close-up role screenplay extra
> director flashback producer shot
> adaptation plot cameraman

1	2	3	4
shot	role	adaptation	director
flashback	_____	_____	_____
_____	_____	_____	_____

2 Choose words from Exercise 1 to complete these sentences.

a) The film is a stylish _____ of a novel by Nevil Shute, with Anthony Hopkins in the _____ of small town cop.

b) Filmed on location, with a _____ of unknown actors, it begins with a _____ of the village at dawn.

c) The complicated _____ develops through the clever use of _____s, which offer us glimpses of the hero's anguished childhood.

d) The _____ has invested millions in this film, but has failed to find a _____ who is capable of realising the book's unique blend of tragedy and farce.

Word formation

Note that the noun from *adapt* is *adaptation*; whereas the noun from *adopt* is *adoption*. Using a dictionary if necessary, complete these sentences by converting the verb form into a noun.

a) I didn't like her (*adapt*) *adaptation* of the novel.

b) This is an interesting (*select*) _____ of Truscott's stories.

c) They are all first rate, without (*except*) _____.

d) This book will satisfy the (*expect*) _____s of his readership.

e) Included in the book is a (*condense*) _____ of his first novel.

f) The critics' initial (*reject*) _____ of this book hardly seems justified . . .

g) . . . and may account for Truscott's (*detest*) _____ of critics ever since.

h) My only (*reserve*) _____ is that the book is not long enough.

LISTENING

1 [▣ 9.1] Listen to an interview with Nicholas Jose, a writer. Number these topics in the order he mentions them.

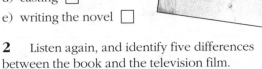

a) shooting the film ☐

b) differences between novel and film ☐

c) writing the script ☐

d) casting ☐

e) writing the novel ☐

2 Listen again, and identify five differences between the book and the television film.

1   *The novel ends in Tiananmen Square in 1986, but the film ends in Tiananmen Square in 1989.*

2   _____

_____

3 _____

4 _____

5 _____

READING

Read the extract from Nicholas Jose's novel
Avenue of Eternal Peace and answer the questions.

The gathering took place in a small concrete-floored apartment on the fifth floor (there was no lift). Dr Song greeted Wally with apologies for the apron under which her tightly cut red dress swelled. She had a rounded face, rounded perm, rolling shoulders and rolypoly middle. She introduced her husband, boyish, bespectacled Dr Rong.

"I can't call you Dr Song and Dr Rong," laughed Wally.

"I have an English name," said the man. "David."

"Fine. And can I just call you Song?" he asked the woman.

David set a cup of tea before Wally and started unfolding the table where they would eat. "Are you accustomed to the life in Peking?"

"Is Peking life accustomed to me? I feel like the proverbial bull most of the time."

"A bull in China?"

"It's an exciting time to be in China, with the Reforms. Do you approve?"

"Life is better now. No one wants to go back."

"That's the one question the China watchers are obsessed with. Will the door close again?"

"There are problems. Resentments. Some intellectuals are unhappy about their position, their low pay. But we cannot go back. Of course, the open policy is not yet entirely realised. China must work towards being open, without becoming too humble or too proud."

"In the West we tend to think of freeing things up as going with human nature - individualism, entrepreneurship, market forces - all instinct. Here it's a conscious ideological move, you're saying."

"Those things are natural here too, but the Party must also learn to allow them."

"To let go control?"

"To find new controls. Chinese people are afraid of chaos. That is where you people are so sophisticated."

"With chaos?"

"With narrowly avoiding it."

The man's smile suggested layers of experience of what was so abstractly discussed.

"Excuse me," David said, "I must prepare food."

(from *Avenue of Eternal Peace* by Nicholas Jose)

1 Read the extract from the novel and mark the lines of direct speech which are spoken by David (*D*) and those spoken by Wally (*W*).

2 Tick the most appropriate answer to the following questions.

a) How would you characterise David's attitude to the reforms?

   i) optimistic ☐   iii) sceptical ☐

   ii) cautious ☐   iv) cynical ☐

b) Wally suggests that, in the West, freedom is:

   i) unconscious ☐   iii) inevitable ☐

   ii) chaotic ☐   iv) instinctive ☐

c) David thinks that, in China, freedom must be:

   i) ideological ☐   iii) avoided ☐

   ii) controlled ☐   iv) sophisticated ☐

LANGUAGE PATTERNS

Infinitives and *-ing* forms

Underline the best form of the verb to complete the text.

When Darryl suggested (*to go/going*) to the movies, I pretended (*to be/being*) interested. But I am beginning (*to get/getting*) uneasy about Darryl's taste in films. Ever since *Terminator 2* I no longer enjoy (*to sit/sitting*) through hours and hours of special effects. Darryl, on the other hand, doesn't mind (*to sit/sitting*) through the bloodiest spectacles, and can endure (*watching/to watch*) any number of sequels to *Robocop* or *Lethal Weapon*. I resolved, however, (*to give/giving*) him one more chance, and I even managed (*to sound/sounding*) interested when he suggested the latest Schwarzenegger epic, especially since he offered (*to pay/paying*). I consented (*to accompany/accompanying*) him, on the condition that next time he would consider (*to join/joining*) me for a night at the opera.

LEARNING GRAMMAR

Modal verbs

1   Choose from the pairs in column B the sentence which most closely matches the meaning of the sentence in column A.

A	**B**
a) You could have phoned me.	i) You might have phoned me. ii) You must have phoned me.
b) English can be difficult.	i) English could be difficult. ii) English is difficult sometimes.
c) The Smiths might come.	i) The Smiths may come. ii) The Smiths can come.
d) I couldn't fix it.	i) I mightn't fix it. ii) I wasn't able to fix it.
e) It couldn't have been him.	i) It can't have been him. ii) It mightn't have been him.
f) You may leave now.	i) You can leave now. ii) You might leave now.
g) It can get cold here in winter.	i) It may get cold here in winter. ii) It sometimes gets cold here in winter.

2   Ability. Choose the correct verb (*can/be able to*) and put it into the correct tense to complete the text.

We gathered at the set at dawn, expecting _____ _____ start shooting as the sun came up. It was a magical morning: on the furthest mountains you _____ see the first rays of the sun turning the snow to gold. A light mist, however, meant that we _____ n't start filming. I realised then that I _____ have spent another half hour in bed. At about seven we _____ start filming, as the sun was now fully out and the mist had dispersed. 'At this rate, I think we _____ _____ finish by midday,' said the director, optimistically.

Things weren't going smoothly, however, and I _____ hear the cameraman cursing under his breath. Apparently he had spent days looking for some vital spare part, but hadn't _____ find one, and now the cold was affecting the camera. By this time the director had given up any hope of _____ finish by lunchtime. Once it got warmer, however, we _____ resume filming again. After a long morning without a break, we _____ finish by three that afternoon, which is not bad, considering we hadn't _____ start filming until nine.

3   Correct these examples of student errors by rewriting them.

a) In the end, a policeman could get the man and he gave the bag back to the woman.

_____

_____

b) If it doesn't rain we will can swim.

_____

c) We couldn't see the temples of Bangkok. Our bus arrived at a temple and five minutes later it would depart.

_____

_____

_____

d) If my money isn't refunded I'll be able to go to a lawyer to resolve the question.

_____

_____

Collocations

Complete the sentences with the appropriate adverbial expressions from the box.

| as well at least possibly by now after all |

1 There was no need to rush. We could have walked _____.
2 I couldn't _____ have phoned you: I didn't have your number!
3 We might _____ have stayed home: the weather was awful.
4 We could've been home _____, if we'd taken a taxi.
5 You might _____ have sent me a postcard: how did I know where you were?

TALKING EFFECTIVELY

[📼 9.2] Read this short scene and, in each sentence marked (*), underline the word that you think carries the main stress. Then listen to the recording to check.

ERIC: You're late.
DEBORAH: I'm sorry. I was held up at the office.
ERIC: *You might have phoned me.
DEBORAH: I phoned Alice and told her.
ERIC: *You might have phoned me!
DEBORAH: Didn't Alice tell you? I asked her to phone you and tell you.
ERIC: Alice? I can't remember. *She might have phoned me.
DEBORAH: Of course she did. I asked her to.
ERIC: That's right. She did. *But you might have phoned me.
DEBORAH: Eric, don't be so childish.

WRITING

Referring back

'Life is better now. No one wants to go back.' 'That's the one question the China watchers are obsessed with . . .'

Words like *question, problem, argument, statement*, etc. are useful for referring back in a general way to earlier parts of a text.

Choose words from the box to complete the examples below.

| narrative refusal boast complaint verdict admission question explanation |

a) 'You are always reading when I talk to you,' she said. I ignored her _____ and left the room.
b) Klaus then went on to say, somewhat shamefacedly, that he had never done a day's work in his life. This _____ both shocked and amused us.
c) 'It won't work because you don't want it to work.' Her _____ of the failure of our scheme was as simple as it was ingenious.
d) '. . . and, to cut a long story short, they lived happily ever after.' Having reached the end of his _____, the miller fell silent again.
e) 'Will you talk?' The officer shook his head. His _____ came as no surprise.
f) 'Not guilty,' said the foreman. The public received the _____ with shouts of joy.
g) 'I have never failed an exam and I never will,' he said. The following week, when the results came out, he was to regret this _____.
h) 'To be, or not to be?' That is the _____.

Star food

VOCABULARY

Kinship terms

1   Match the term in column A with its definition in column B.

A	B
a) niece	1 the sister of your husband or wife; or the wife of your brother
b) great aunt	
c) godmother	2 your sister by one parent only
d) second cousin	3 the unmarried sister of your father or mother
e) sister-in-law	4 your wife's or husband's female child by a previous marriage
f) maiden aunt	
g) stepdaughter	5 the daughter of your brother or sister
h) half-sister	6 the child of your parent's cousin
	7 your grandparent's sister
	8 woman who sponsors a baptised child

2   What is the male version of each of the above terms?

a) _____   e) _____

b) _____   f) _____

c) _____   g) _____

d) _____   h) _____

3   In the following puzzle, who is 'this man'?

Sisters and brothers have I none
But this man's father is my father's son.

Answer: _____

READING

"FATHER CHRISTMAS and I", said Ruby to her children, "have a special relationship." That was in 1971, when the boys were twelve, ten, seven and two respectively. Billy, Joshua, Jason and little Ben.

"Does that mean no presents this year?" asked Billy, who had a nervous disposition, and red hair like his father. Sometimes he was difficult to like.

"You mean a special relationship like between Britain and the US?" asked Joshua, who had been categorized as a gifted child. It had its drawbacks: he got called brainbox and was bullied in the playground.

"Does that mean he's going to be our new Daddy?" asked Jason, who lived in fear of some terrible event, which would come along and confound his life yet further.

And little Ben said nothing at all. He wasn't speaking yet. The clinic recommended he see a child development specialist and Ruby was putting it off. She had enough to do, as it was.

"It means," said Ruby, "Father Christmas may put the presents down the chimney on New Year's Eve rather than Christmas Eve because I don't get paid till the last Friday of every month."

Ruby had a part-time job. She worked in the office of the local secondary school. The family lived in Garton, a small town in the new County of Avon, as unexciting as its name.

"There's no such thing as Father Christmas anyway," said Billy.

"There is so," said Joshua.

"Fancy you being ten and believing that," said Billy.

Jason said, "I know there's no Father Christmas because I waited up one night with a torch and it was Dad dressed up in a red gown with cotton wool."

"What you saw," said Ruby, briskly, "was Father Christmas dressed up as Dad."

And little Ben said nothing at all.

"Anyway," said Ruby, "he told me he'd come on New Year's Eve, and he wouldn't lie to me because I'm his wife."

"Is that the special relationship?" asked Joshua.

"Yes," said Ruby. "I'm Mother Christmas and you can see I'm true."

(from *The Search for Mother Christmas* by Fay Weldon)

Key

Unit 1

VOCABULARY

a) Remind b) memorise c) memoirs d) reminds
e) memorial f) memory g) remember h) memory
i) remind j) memories

LISTENING

1
a) 2 b) 4 c) 5 d) 1 e) 3

2
b) False c) True d) False e) False

3
See tapescript page 78

READING

1
A sensory   B episodic

2
a) recalls b) brought back

TALKING EFFECTIVELY

I re<u>member</u>, I re<u>member</u>,
The <u>house</u> where I was <u>born</u>,
The little <u>wind</u>ow where the <u>sun</u>
Came <u>peep</u>ing in at <u>morn</u>;
He never came a <u>wink</u> too <u>soon</u>,
Nor <u>brought</u> too long a <u>day</u>,
But now I often <u>wish</u> the <u>night</u>
Had <u>borne</u> my breath <u>away</u>!

LEARNING GRAMMAR

Error correction

Suggested answer
Last Sunday night the doorbell rang. I opened the door
and I was very surprised to see my brother standing
there. He had changed a lot, but he had the same smile
as always. He was taller and thinner. He had a lot of hair
but he looked very interesting: he had always been
good-looking. Now he's twenty-five years old, he's a
lawyer, and he works for Johns & Smith Company. We
talked all night and we reminisced about a lot of things.

Verbs

2 is   3 have never been   4 am climbing   5 fills (or
will fill)   6 had been hiking   7 reached   8 had
crossed   9 was   10 would descend   11 would lead
12 planned (or were planning, had planned, had been
planning)   13 felt (or were feeling)   14 looked (or
was looking)   15 reached   16 emerged   17 was
18 had lead   19 was   20 turned   21 had snowed
(or had been snowing)   22 set   23 stood
24 bolted   25 bordered

Nouns

a) anybody; some interesting people
b) a beautiful blue-eyed girl
c) Everyone; other countries
d) each other (or one another); our mother's house; her
60th birthday
e) our group of friends
f) the dog (or a dog, dogs); man's best friend
g) some very bad news
h) double-decker bus; the top deck
i) a famous scientist

Unit 2

VOCABULARY

1
b) 5 c) 4 d) 2 e) 6 f) 3 g) 1

2
b) broad-minded c) thick-skinned d) good-looking
e) kind-hearted f) long-suffering g) smooth-talking

TALKING EFFECTIVELY

a) level-<u>headed</u> b) <u>long</u>-suffering c) thick-<u>skinned</u>
d) <u>Smooth</u>-talking e) <u>kind</u>-hearted f) <u>level</u>-headed
g) <u>broad</u>-minded h) broad-<u>minded</u>

READING

1
a) 'I didn't recognize Eva Kay...'
d) 'Dad couldn't even find his way to Beckenham...'
c) 'Two men near me glanced at each other as if they
wanted to laugh.'
d) 'The nervousness he'd shown earlier...'

2
A

3
c)

4
a) ii b) ii c) i d) i e) i

LEARNING GRAMMAR

a) ii b) i) c) i) d) i e) i f) ii g) ii h) i

LANGUAGE PATTERNS

Reporting verbs

1
a) insist; emphasise; warn; announce
b) instruct; warn; reassure; remind
c) instruct; warn; remind; order

2
b) He reassured us (that) it wouldn't hurt.
c) He warned us (that) it might be dangerous.
d) He reminded us not to resist or He reminded us (that)
we shouldn't resist.
e) My father announced (that) the session had begun.
f) He ordered the women to raise their arms.
g) He instructed Eva to breathe out.
h) He emphasised (that) we would need to concentrate.
i) Dad insisted (that) Eva should relax.

WRITING

Suggested answer
Before you start, sit comfortably and breathe deeply. *Now*, stand up with your arms by your side. *Next,* touch your toes. *Having done that,* stretch your arms above you. *At the same time*, raise one leg. *Then,* lower it and raise the other leg. *Finally*, touch your toes again. *And then* sit down.

Unit 3

LEARNING GRAMMAR

Would

b) was going to   c) neither   d) used to   e) was going to   f) used to   g) used to; neither   h) neither i) was going to

Future in the past

a) was going to   b) was meeting   c) would have d) were going to   e) were to   f) would forget g) was to write   h) was going to

TALKING EFFECTIVELY

a) optional   b) stressed   c) optional   d) optional e) stressed   f) optional   g) optional

READING

3
a) iii   b) i   c) iii   d) ii   e) i   f) ii

4
'I wouldn't swim at Bondi.' 'I'd love to have that on tap.'

LISTENING

	Place	Activities	Food
1	Venice, Greece and Turkey	School cruise Visit to Blue Mosque and Muslim Bazaar	Oranges Tea with sugar
2	Maine, USA	Sailing Swimming Clearing up	Lobster Steamed clams Corn on the cob
3	Catalina Island, USA	Ferry boat trip Playing on the beach	Picnic Hamburgers, hot dogs and french fries Candy apples, cotton candy and popcorn
4	Florida, USA	Playing on beaches	Saltwater taffee Orange juice Seafood

VOCABULARY

a) sea   b) water   c) wind   d) sand   e) sun
f) salt

LANGUAGE PATTERNS

a) shopping   b) and see   c) fishing   d) and eat e) and do   f) skiing   g) and ask   h) and camp i) camping

WRITING

just; earlier; Meanwhile; Presently; Then; Later; At the same time; Subsequently; beforehand; Afterwards

Unit 4

READING

1
b) What proportion of the world's mail, telexes and cables are in English?
c) What proportion of scientific publications are in English?
d) What proportion of the EC's administrative budget goes on translation and interpretation?
e) How much money does the teaching of English as a foreign language make in Britain?
f) How many people speak English worldwide?
g) How many people will be speaking English by the year 2000?
h) How many hours of English instruction will a Japanese child who finishes secondary school have had?
i) How many Japanese students undertake courses in America?

2
a)   b)   d)

LEARNING GRAMMAR

1
DO YOU SPEAK Ø JAPANESE?
Ø Help is on the horizon. *The* growth in Ø Japanese instruction around *the* world is far faster than *the* growth in Ø English. Between 1967 and 1984, *the* number of Ø foreigners studying Ø Japanese increased from 37,000 to almost 600,000. *The* Japanese Ministry of Ø Education predicts that *the* number of Ø foreigners studying in Ø Japan will increase four-fold by 2000 from *the* present 25,000. On *the* opposite edge of *the* Pacific rim, *the* number of Ø students learning Ø Japanese at Ø American colleges and universities increased by 45% to 23,500. Worldwide, 80% of *the* people learning Ø Japanese are Asian, however, and only take it up as a third language after Ø English.
3
1c   2b   3a   4b   5a   6b   7b   8c (generic refernce)
9c   10b   11a   12b   13b

VOCABULARY

2
a) rule of thumb   b) rules and regulations
c) working to rule   d) rulebook   e) As a rule
f) stretch/bend the rules   g) the exception that proves the rule

WRITING

Dear Frieda,

Did you *receive* my last letter? I've been *hoping* you would write: I'm *dying* to hear from you. I'm *writing chiefly* to tell you an *unbelievable piece* of news: I finally *achieved* what I have been trying to do all year – I passed my *driving* test! What a *relief*! A year ago, when I started *taking* lessons, it seemed *inconceivable* that one day I would actually get it. Tonight I am *celebrating* with some friends: *their* surprise is nearly as great as mine.

Well, that's my news. How are you? It's *freezing* here – good weather for skiing, but I spend most of the time *lying* in bed – as you know I am a *believer* in *leisure*!

Lots of love,

Sheila.

LANGUAGE PATTERNS

1
b) She was heard to speak favourably of the new grammar.
c) I was made to learn spelling rules by heart.
d) The pupils were seen to be enjoying the lesson.
e) The new materials are said to be easy to use.
f) The students weren't made to do homework.
g) The learners were heard to speak French fluently.

2
a) ii   b) i   c) ii   d) i   e) ii

TALKING EFFECTIVELY

a) i) <u>per</u>fect   ii) per<u>fect</u>   b) i) de<u>sert</u>   ii) <u>desert</u>
c) i) <u>rebel</u>   ii) re<u>bel</u>   d) i) pre<u>sent</u>   ii) <u>present</u>
e) i) <u>export</u>   ii) ex<u>port</u>

Unit 5

LEARNING GRAMMAR

1
told; had had; was; was; had described; was; had noticed; had been; was; had been

2
a) My mother *told* me that my boyfriend, Andrew, *had had an* accident and he *was* in the General Hospital.
b) When we *arrived home* and I opened the door, *other* friends were *already inside*. They *had prepared a* party and I *was surprised*.
c) When we arrived, the train *had left* the station and we *waited* (or *had to wait*) three long hours until the next train arrived.
d) I realised that they *had fallen* in love.
e) I didn't realise it was so late and the underground *had (already) stopped working*.
f) *Man has been* destroying the planet *for* centuries.
g) *This* afternoon my cousin *killed his mother's cat* because *it* was in the road and *he didn't see it* (or *he hadn't seen it*).

LISTENING

Coincidence 1: Spontaneous association
Coincidence 2: Mind over matter
Coincidence 3: Small world

VOCABULARY

2
a) chance it   b) Chances are (that)   c) stands a good/fair chance   d) on the off chance (that)
e) chanced upon   f) by chance

LANGUAGE PATTERNS

b) Terry reminded Tony to take his bus pass.
c) Imogen reminded the children that the last train left at 10.30.
d) Rachel persuaded Nigel that Lima was the capital of Chile.
e) The boss required Smith to work late on Friday.
f) Basil warned Sybil not to mention the war.
g) The police warned tourists that there were pickpockets operating in the area.
h) The captain required (or warned) the passengers to return to their seats and fasten their safety belts.
i) The zookeeper warned the children not to feed the animals.
j) Jim persuaded Martin to lend him £5.
k) The guard required the visitors to show their tickets.

READING

1
a) True   b) True   c) True   d) False   e) False
f) False   g) True   h) True   i) False   j) False

2
c)

TALKING EFFECTIVELY

1
b) six   c) tin   d) sieve   e) Bill   f) singing
g) Whitman   h) kitten   j) chips   k) a slipper

2
b) I; Five; live; Isle; Wight
c) Sign; Times
d) windy; revived; Bryan
e) Miles; wild; side
f) title; White
g) xylophone

WRITING

Once; earlier; No sooner; whereupon; Later; immediately; meanwhile; whereupon

Unit 6

VOCABULARY

Word formation; Compound nouns derived from multi-part verbs

1
b) 5   c) 1 2 4   d) 3   e) 3 4   f) 1

2
b) shutdown   c) workout   d) drawback
e) turnover   f) run-up

3
b) upset   c) outset   d) upturn   e) output
f) onset   g) input   h) uptake

Scale and limit words

It was an *absolutely* freezing day when we arrived in Berlin, and I was *extremely* unhappy, as I hadn't bothered to pack warm clothes. We were taken to Potsdam on the first day, and although the palace was *extremely* interesting, we had an *absolutely* disgusting meal, compounded by the fact that the waiter was *extremely* rude. The only consolation was that it was *extremely* cheap. Nevertheless, we were both in an *extremely* bad mood by the time we got back to the city. The following day was *absolutely* marvellous. Because it was still *extremely* cold, we decided to do the museums, my favourite being the Antiquities Museum with the bust of Nefertiti: an *absolutely* beautiful piece, although I was *extremely* surprised to discover that she has one eye missing.

TALKING EFFECTIVELY

a) Negative b) Positive c) Positive d) Negative
e) Negative f) Positive g) Positive h) Negative

LEARNING GRAMMAR

Adverb order

1
b) She plays tennis well.
c) Seldom do I do the housework.
d) Up came the firemen.
e) I don't often go to the cinema.
f) Rarely does he open his mouth.
g) Only then did she understand.
h) Around the corner came the bus.
i) Never have I eaten so well.

2
Incey Wincey Spider
Climbing *up* the spout.
Down came the rain
And washed poor Incey *out.*
Out came the sun
Away went all the rain.
Incey Wincey Spider
Climbed the spout again.

Adjective order

b) plastic c) white d) ball-point e) woollen
f) beach g) Californian

READING

1
a) d)

2
a) Mrs S., an intelligent woman in her sixties, has suffered a massive stroke, affecting the deeper and back portions of her right cerebral hemisphere. *She has perfectly preserved intelligence – and humour.*
b) She sometimes complains to the nurses that they have not put dessert or coffee on her tray. When they say, "But, Mrs S., it is right there, on the left", she seems not to understand what they say, and does not look to the left. If her head is gently turned, so that the dessert comes into sight, in the preserved right half of her visual field, she says, "Oh, there it is – it wasn't there before." She has totally lost the idea of "left", both with regard to the world and her own body. Sometimes she complains that her portions are too small, but this is because she only eats from the right half of her plate. *It does not occur to her that it has a left half as well.* Sometimes, she will put on lipstick, and make up the right half of her face,

leaving the left half completely neglected: it is almost impossible to treat these things, because her attention cannot be drawn to them and she has no conception that they are wrong. She knows it intellectually, and can understand, and laugh; but it is impossible for her to know it directly.
c) Knowing it intellectually, she has worked out strategies for dealing with her imperfection. She cannot look left, directly, she cannot turn left, so what she does is to turn right – and right through a circle. *Thus she requested, and was given, a rotating wheelchair.* And now if she cannot find something which she knows should be there, she swivels to the right, through a circle, until it comes into view. She finds this signally successful if she cannot find her coffee or dessert.
d) It would seem far simpler for her to rotate the plate than rotate herself. *She agrees, and has tried this – or at least tried to try it.* But it is oddly difficult, it does not come naturally, whereas whizzing round in her chair does, because her looking, her attention, her spontaneous movements and impulses, are all now exclusively and instinctively to the right.

LANGUAGE PATTERNS

b) They appeared not to be enjoying themselves. (same)
c) Samuel didn't agree to speak. (different)
d) It tends not to rain much in spring. (same)
e) I expected not to recognise you. (same)
f) He didn't manage to do the dishes. (different)
g) I intend not to talk to him, if I can help it. (same)
h) He didn't pretend to laugh. (different)
i) The government didn't promise to raise the interest rate. (different)
j) I wish not to be disturbed. (same)

WRITING

a) colon b) semi-colon c) colon d) colon
e) semi-colon f) semi-colon g) colon

Unit 7

VOCABULARY

1

Table 1	copy	facsimile	replica	imitation	fake	counterfeit	forgery
both legal and illegal	✓						
usually legal		✓	✓	✓			
usually illegal					✓	✓	✓

Table 2	copy	facsimile	replica	imitation	fake	counterfeit	forgery
things in general	✓						
money						✓	
paintings	✓				✓		
documents	✓	✓					✓
3-dimensional objects			✓				
signatures	✓						✓
textiles/ fabrics	✓			✓			

2

to imitate; to fax; to fake; to replicate; to counterfeit; to forge

3

a) forge   b) imitation   c) facsimile   d) copy
e) counterfeit   f) fake   g) replica

LISTENING

1

b) 2   c) 7   d) 3   e) 1   f) 5   g) 2   h) 7   i) 2
j) 2   k) 5   l) 6

2

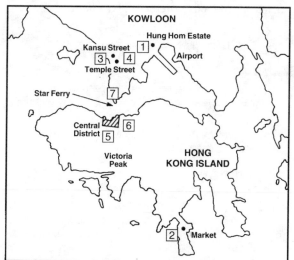

LEARNING GRAMMAR

1

b) As he had no alarm clock, he overslept.
c) Once they had found somewhere to park, they were able to take their time.
d) Now that we have decided on the film, we'd better think of a restaurant.
e) If children are ignored by their parents, they grow anxious.
f) Since he had lost the keys, he had to break down the door.
g) Seeing that Simon was married, Helen settled for David.

2

b) Having practised a few times, he got very good at it.
c) Having been overseas, you ought to settle down.
d) The doctor having said nothing, she felt less worried.
e) It being a Sunday, she slept in.
f) Given a coat of paint, it will look like new.
g) Being our local MP, you might like to get involved.

3

b) The house having been freshly renovated, she decided to buy it.
c) Once it had been stripped and cleaned, we realised that the painting was a genuine masterpiece. or Stripped and cleaned, the painting was a genuine masterpiece, we realised.
d) It being cold and rainy, I decided to stay in.
e) The burgundy having been in the cellar for nearly a century, our host announced that it was time to drink it. or As it had been in the cellar...

f) It being the first book she had published, I read it with some interest. or As it was the first book...
g) The movie having been filmed in black and white, the audience soon lost interest in it. or As the movie had been filmed...
h) Since/As it had been considered by critics to be a work of genius, we were looking forward to seeing it.
i) His wife served the lamb, which had been marinated in wine and fresh herbs.

4
a) 4 b) 5 c) 2 d) 6 e) 1 f) 3

LANGUAGE PATTERNS

1
a) different. In the first example, the discussing followed the stopping, while in the second example the discussing came first. b) Same c) Same d) Different. In the first example, 'turning the water off' is something I did in order to achieve a desired result. In the second example, I attempted to turn the water off, but didn't succeed.
e) Different. In the first example, remembering comes after 'leaving the keys'. In the second example, he remembered and then he left the keys. f) Same

2
raining; reading; to climb; having; to avoid; to leap; to consider; to inform; cleaning

WRITING

Not having flown into Hong Kong before, I was unprepared for the sudden steep descent to the airport. Visibly shaking and clutching the armrests, I watched the tenement buildings flashing by. You could practically reach out and touch the washing that hung from the balconies. Noticing my terror, my neighbour leant over and said: 'This is nothing compared to taking-off!' Remembering that I was booked to fly on to Beijing later that same evening, I didn't thank him for this observation. The plane touched down without so much as a bump. Embarrassed by my display of nerves but relieved that we had at least landed safely, I disembarked, looking forward to my few hours' stopover in Hong Kong.

Unit 8

READING

1
1 academic 2 journalist 3 bureaucrat 4 editor
5 businesswoman

2
a) False b) False c) True d) True e) True
f) True g) False

3
a) ground-breaking b) mainstream c) rocky
d) transition e) re-invent oneself

VOCABULARY

Suffixes

1
feminism; journalism; activism; idealism; pragmatism
Journalism is the odd one out, since this refers to a practice while the others refer to beliefs, principles.

2
b) dentist c) realist (realism) d) cyclist
e) humorist f) sexist (sexism) g) zoologist
h) florist i) pacifist (pacifism) j) flautist

Nouns into verbs

head; back; stomach; eyeing; fingered; handed; headed

LEARNING GRAMMAR

b) Will you be needing the car tomorrow? 7
c) Will you be wanting the butter immediately? 6
d) Will you be going to the supermarket this morning? 5
e) Will you be wearing your pearl earrings tonight? 1
f) Will you be passing the post office this afternoon? 3
g) Will you be seeing Maria on Monday? 2

LANGUAGE PATTERNS

Multi-part verbs: Transitive

1
b) We have been asked to sort *out* the problem of the exam papers that were thrown away.
c) She told *off* the children for smoking. or She told the children *off* for smoking.
d) The police are trying to track *down* the woman, her two accomplices, and the driver of the van.
e) Ann Summers can't figure *out* what to do with her life.
f) If we can't afford a party, let's call it *off*.
g) This vote could bring *down* the government. or This vote could bring the government *down*.
h) Why don't you talk it *over* with your flatmate?
i) I can't spin *out* this exercise much longer. or I can't spin this exercise *out* much longer.

2
resolve b) extend i) discuss h) accomodate a)
defeat g) decide e) reprimand c) locate d)

Adverbs and prepositions

1
a) Preposition b) Adverb c) Preposition
d) Preposition e) Adverb f) Preposition
g) Adverb h) Adverb i) Adverb j) Preposition

2
erase g) refuse i) to put it on to see if it fits h)
decorate b) chase and catch e)

TALKING EFFECTIVELY

a) Which applicant did they turn <u>down</u>?
b) Which street did you <u>turn</u> down?
c) You're going visiting? Who are you going to <u>call</u> on?
d) You want to use the phone? Who are you going to call <u>up</u>?

e) What bridge did the cars <u>pass</u> on?
f) What news did the doctor pass <u>on</u>?
g) What door did you <u>knock</u> on?
h) Which boxer did you knock <u>out</u>?
   In multi-part verbs final adverbs are normally
   stressed; final prepositions are not normally stressed.

WRITING

1
a) I studied Latin and Greek. The former taught me how
   to think. The latter taught me how to feel.
b) We visited Naples and Florence. We were seduced by
   food in the former, and by art in the latter.
c) It was in Simla that we met Tusker and his wife. I
   didn't think much of the latter.
d) Foreign travel is nothing compared to the pleasure of
   reading good books. I would happily forego the
   former if I could spend my life doing the latter.
e) I have already written to you about the possibility of
   your opening the exhibition as well as writing an
   introduction to the catalogue. With regard to the
   former, there is already a great deal of interest.

2
above; enclosed; this; thus; previous; there; The latter;
then; In this way

3
1 CTEFLA Course
2 fees information accompanying the letter
3 the deposit of £100
4 sending the deposit by means of a bank transfer
5 a letter sent before this one
6 to the Institute
7 The No 45 bus
8 at 4.00
9 By going for a drink

Unit 9

VOCABULARY

1

1	**2**	**3**	**4**
shot	role	adaptation	director
flashback	extra	screenplay	producer
close-up	cast	plot	cameraman

2
a) adaptation; role   b) cast;shot   c) plot; flashback
d) producer;director

Word formation

b) selection   c) exception   d) expectation
e) condensation   f) rejection   g) detestation
h) reservation

LISTENING

1
a) 4)   b) 3   c) 2   d) 5   e) 1

2
2 Australian Wally Frith changes to Englishman Will
  Flint
3 title changes
4 doctor's son, not wife, died

5 Wally returns to Australia alone, but Will rescues a
  girl student and takes her back to Australia with him.

READING

1
(Wally) 'I can't call you Dr Song and Dr Rong.'
(David) 'I have an English name. David.'
(Wally) 'Fine. And can I just call you Song?'
(David) 'Are you accustomed to the life in Peking?'
(Wally) 'Is Peking life accustomed to me? I feel like the
proverbial bull most of the time.'
(David) 'A bull in China?'
(Wally) 'It's an exciting time to be in China, with the
Reforms. Do you approve?'
(David) 'Life is better now. No one wants to go back.'
(Wally) 'That's the one question the China watchers are
obsessed with. Will the door close again?'
(David) 'There are problems. Resentments. Some
intellectuals are unhappy about their position, their low
pay. But we cannot go back. Of course, the open policy is
not yet entirely realised. China must work towards being
open, without becoming too humble or too proud."
(Wally) 'In the West we tend to think of freeing things
up as going with human nature – individualism,
entrepreneurship, market forces – all instinct. Here it's a
conscious ideological move, you're saying.'
(David) 'Those things are natural here too, but the Party
must also learn to allow them.'
(Wally) 'To let go control?'
(David) 'To find new controls. Chinese people are afraid
of chaos. That is where you people are so sophisticated.'
(Wally) 'With chaos?'
(David) 'With narrowly avoiding it. ... Excuse me, I must
prepare food.'

2
a) ii   b) iv   c) ii

LANGUAGE PATTERNS

going; to be; to get; sitting; sitting; watching; to give; to
sound; to pay; to accompany; joining

LEARNING GRAMMAR

Modal verbs

1
a) i)   b) ii)   c) i)   d) ii)   e) i)   f) i)   g) ii)

2
to be able to; could; could; could; were able to; will be
able to; could; been able to; being able to; were able to;
were able to; been able to

3
a) In the end, a policeman was able to get the man and
   he gave the bag back to the woman.
b) If it doesn't rain we will be able to swim.
c) We weren't able to see the temples of Bangkok. Our
   bus would arrive at a temple and five minutes later it
   would depart.
d) If my money isn't refunded I'll have to go to a lawyer
   to resolve the question.

Collocations

a) after all   b) possibly   c) as well   d) by now   e) at least

TALKING EFFECTIVELY

phoned; me; might; you

WRITING

a) complaint   b) admission   c) explanation
d) narrative   e) refusal   f) verdict   g) boast
h) question

Unit 10

VOCABULARY

1
a) 5   b) 7   c) 8   d) 6   e) 1   f) 3   g) 4   h) 2

2
a) nephew   b) great uncle   c) godfather
d) second cousin   e) brother-in-law   f) no equivalent
g) stepson   h) half-brother

3
'This man' is the speaker's son.

READING

1
a) True   b) True   c) False   d) False

2
a) 4   b) 3   c) 2   d) 1

3
a) 'She had enough to do, as it was.'
b) Because of her response to Joshua's doubts about father Christmas being real: 'What you saw...was Father Christmas dressed up as Dad.'
c) She was putting off taking Ben to the child specialist.
d) Garton was 'as unexciting as its name.'
e) The fact that she can't buy Christmas presents until she gets paid – this suggests she has little or no money to spend.

LANGUAGE PATTERNS

1
a) The bank manager has written a letter to me.
b) I showed the letter to my husband.
c) The bank had offered us a loan.
d) They had lent my husband and me £5000.
e) It cost us a lot.
f) We owe the bank £1000.
g) We will send it to them.

2
a) Todd lent Ted £5. Ted lent Todd £5.
b) The woman gave the man a flower. The man gave the woman a flower.
c) The priest offered the youth to the dragon. The priest offered the dragon to the youth. The youth offered the priest to the dragon. The youth offered the dragon to the priest. The dragon offered the youth to the priest. The dragon offered the priest to the youth.
d) They sent her to him. They sent him to her.
e) The prince showed the princess the frog. The prince showed the frog the princess. The princess showed the prince the frog. The princess showed the frog the prince. The frog showed the prince the princess. The frog showed the princess the prince.

LEARNING GRAMMAR

1
a) Although   b) though   c) Still   d) whereas
e) While   f) While   g) Though   h) However

2
a) though   b) while   c) still

WRITING

1
Although; And; however; Despite the fact that; On the other hand; Again; but; And; yet; Moreover; even though

2
5   7   1   4   3   6   2
The judge is the mugger's mother.

Unit 11

VOCABULARY

1
b) brightness   c) dazzling   d) palette   e) emerald
f) faded   g) fade

2
a) shadow   b) shade   c) dull   d) dye   e) red
f) faded   g) glitters

READING

1
c

2
g   c   f   b   a   e   d

3
a) True   b) False   c) True   d) True   e) False

5
a) 3   b) 6   c) 7   d) 1   e) 4   f) 2   g) 5

LISTENING

1
a) 3   b) 5   c) 1   d) 2   e) 4

2

Colour	Food	Good for (illness)
orange	carrots, pumpkins, apricots, oranges, peaches	heart, bones, teeth, lungs
blue	grapes, prunes, blueberries	burns, emotional disorders, stress
yellow	corn, bananas, lemons, eggs	stomach upset
red	tomatoes, cherries, beets	blood problems

LEARNING GRAMMAR

1

1 This   2 It   3 This   4 This   5 this   6 This   7 it
8 it   9 This   10 it   11 this   12 it

2

b) It's obvious that carrots are good for you.
c) It's funny how different colours affect me.
d) It's doubtful whether colours have healing properties.
e) It's extraodinary how people heal faster in green rooms.
f) It's possible that some colours are stimulating.
g) It would be strange eating an all-yellow meal.
h) It's unlikely that prunes help you sleep.
i) It's not surprising that some people find colour therapy hard to believe.

LANGUAGE PATTERNS

After ten months at Innisfree I find *it* hard to believe what *it* was like living in the city. *It* is now evening and I sit watching the linnets as the sunlight fades. How I love *it* when the thin crescent of the moon hangs above the lake: it is a sight I will never forget. I hope I will never grow tired of it: I think *it* unlikely. I have never experienced such peace and happiness. I owe *it* all to my decision that day nearly a year ago when, standing on the grey city pavement, I found *it* suddenly unbearable and resolved to leave at once. Now, looking back, I wonder how I put up with *it* for so long.

TALKING EFFECTIVELY

I will arise and <u>go</u> now, and <u>go</u> to Innisfree,
And a small cabin build there, of clay and wattles made:
Nine bean-<u>rows</u> shall I have there, and a hive for the honey bee,
And live <u>alone</u> in the bee-loud glade.

And I shall have some peace there, for peace comes dropping <u>slow</u>,
Dropping from the veils of the morning to where the cricket sings;
There midnight's all a glimmer, and noon a purple <u>glow</u>,
And evening full of the linnet's wings.

I will arise and <u>go</u> now, for always night and day
I hear lake water lapping with <u>low</u> sounds by the shore;
While I stand on the <u>road</u>way, or on the pavements grey
I hear it in the deep heart's core.

Spelling: -o (go); -ow (slow); -o-e (alone); -oa- (road)

WRITING

Suggested answer:
William Butler Yeats was born into an artistic family in Ireland in 1865. He developed an early interest, reflected in his poetry, in Irish folklore and the occult. He helped establish the Irish National Theatre, where many of his plays were performed. He also wrote prose. His later poetry is considered some of the greatest 20th century verse in English. In 1923 he won the Nobel Prize for literature, and he died in 1939. (75 words)

Unit 12

VOCABULARY

1

a) 4   b) 6   c) 2   d) 5   e) 1   f) 3

2

a) to take the bull by the horns
b) to kill two birds with one stone
c) let the cat out of the bag

READING

1

a) geese   b) gander   c) gosling   d) honking and hissing

2

a) iii, iv   b) i iv v

3

b

4

c

5

a) bereaved   b) became bogged down   c) spot
d) persistent   e) epitomize   f) fidelity   g) beheld
h) hatching   i) grazing   j) stationary

LANGUAGE PATTERNS

b) Anyone supposing that this story is invented doesn't know much about animals.
c) Take the case of a person drowning.
d) Anyone trying to touch her kittens would be attacked.
e) Geese living in the wild seldom experience this problem.
f) Anyone hearing of a similar case, please let me know.
g) The dog bit the woman maltreating it.
h) Any animal living with humans will think that it is human too.
i) Have you ever heard of a goose following a lawnmower around?

LEARNING GRAMMAR

1

b) box of matches   c) cup of tea   d) mailbags
e) matchbox   f) bottle of wine   g) wine bottle
h) teacup

2

b) mousetrap   c) strawberry icecream   d) indoor plants   e) card table   f) five-pound note   g) pearl necklace   h) roadside   i) flowerbed   j) two-litre bottle   k) midday sun   l) forty-hour week
m) toothpaste

3

b) Chase death probe   b) Bomb case man cleared
c) Pit strike threat riddle   e) Bread price rise shock

4

a) There will be some world cup boat races.
b) The course fees are £900 for two months.
c) When we arrived at the airport the hotel taxi wasn't there.

d) He stuck the explosives near the hinges of the door of the safe.
e) One day he decided to leave his bachelor life.
f) First I had to go to my friend's house.
g) We have also a bus network.
h) I've got the house key and I can return at night when I want.

WRITING

A is the real story.

The ambiguities in 1–4 are:
1 Intended meaning: Westinghouse gives a firm the rights to manufacture a robot.
   Unintended meaning: Westinghouse gave a robot the rights to a firm.
2 Intended meaning: Talks (negotiations) with teachers in Johnson are going very slowly.
   Unintended meaning: There is a teacher in Johnson who talks very slow(ly).
3 Intended meaning: A bus coordinator who died recently has been remembered.
   Unintended meaning: A coordinator of buses that ran late has been remembered.
4 Intended meaning: The French have offered a reward for the capture of terrorist(s).
   Unintended meaning: The French have offered a terrorist a reward.

Unit 13

VOCABULARY

Multi-part verbs

a) The sound of the ice-cream van took Esther back to her childhood. (must be separated)
b) They look so similar I can't tell them apart. (must be separated)
c) Tony stood his girlfriend up. (must be separated)
d) Why don't you take back those empty bottles? or ...take those empty bottles back? (optional)
e) Wayne is always pushing the other children around. (must be separated)
f) Let's bring forward the date of the meeting. or ...bring the date of the meeting forward. (optional)
g) The doctor put my tiredness down to lack of sleep. (must be separated)

The unusual

	slang	people	things	negative
zany		✓		
eccentric		✓		
mad		✓		✓
unconventional		✓	✓	
dotty	✓	✓		
weird		✓	✓	✓
crazy		✓	✓	✓
odd		✓		✓
barmy	✓	✓		✓
obsessive		✓		✓
insane		✓		✓

1

2
A possible order might be:
unconventional -> odd -> weird -> crazy -> mad -> insane

LISTENING

1
a) Obsessive-Compulsive Disorder   b) 'Washers' and 'checkers'   c) A bout (short period) of depression   d) Between four and five million   e) Electric shock therapy or lobotomy   f) Not entirely   g) Behaviour therapy

2
Suggested answer:
OCD stands for Obsessive-Compulsive Disorder and is an affliction which manifests itself in obsessive behaviour, such as repeated washing or checking. It is often started by a bout of depression. It is estimated that between four and five million people suffer from OCD in the United States. OCD was traditionally treated by either electric shock therapy or lobotomy. Certain drugs seem to help but nowadays the best form of treatment is considered to be behaviour therapy. (77 words)

READING

1
c f

2
a) True   b) True   c) False   d) False   e) True
f) True   g) False

3
a) He is described as a family man.
b) His father made him a special table.
c) He tried every therapy available.
d) 'They just took our money.'
e) His mother destroyed the special table.

4
a) indulgence   b) compulsion   c) compassion
d) revulsion

5
a) handicapped   b) depressed   c) obsessed

6
a) contaminated   b) immersed   c) invaded
d) engulfed

LANGUAGE PATTERNS

Infinitives and -ing forms: review

a) to believe   b) to be   c) living   d) to remember
e) to do

Result clauses

a) It was such a hot day we abandoned sightseeing.
b) The film was so offensive we walked out.
c) So tired was she that she slept for 14 hours.
d) The pool was so crowded that we went home.
e) So successful was the business that they took on more staff.
f) It was such a noisy party the police were called.

LEARNING GRAMMAR

Cause, purpose, result

a) Owing to its bad design ... or Owing to the fact that it had been badly designed the bridge collapsed.
b) She gave up work so as to look after her mother. or ... so she could look after her mother.
c) Since Ellen has flu, we've decided not to go out.
d) As a result of missing the train we had to walk.
e) They've taken a taxi on account of the rain.
f) As you're a friend of mine I can tell you.
g) Because of his drinking, she left him.

Linking ideas: defining and non-defining relative clauses

a) where   b) whose   c) whom   d) who   e) when
f) whom   g) whose   h) which   i) where   j) who
k) where   l) which

TALKING EFFECTIVELY

a) Defining   b) Non-defining   c) Non-defining
d) Defining   e) Non-defining   f) Defining
g) Defining   h) Non-defining

WRITING

1

a) The children who went to the ballet enjoyed themselves.
b) The children, who went to the ballet, enjoyed themselves.
c) The passengers, who had eaten fish, were ill.
d) The passengers who had eaten fish were ill.
e) I'm going to visit my brother, who lives in New York.
f) I'm going to visit my brother who lives in New York.
g) The buildings which have been restored look lovely.
h) The buildings, which have been restored, look lovely.

2
Suggested answer:
A A duchess plans to abseil from a 150-foot high hospital roof this weekend in order to raise funds for charity.
B The stunt by the duchess, who is the sister of the Marquess of Bath, will mark the start of National Meningitis Awareness Week.
C 'It is the scariest thing I can imagine which is why I am doing it,' said the 60-year-old duchess, wife of the 11th duke, whose family seat is at Badminton Park.
D The duchess, who is well-known for her unconventional behaviour, recently swam in a piranha-infested river during a trip to Brazil.

Unit 14

LEARNING GRAMMAR

Substitution

b) not   c) one   d) did   e) so   f) one   g) so
h) do   i) mine   j) not   k) do

Ellipsis

1
b) We decided we would educate the girls exactly as we would the boys.

c) She never finished her degree though now she wishes she had.
d) Margaret takes the girls on holiday and Mortimer the boys.
e) Libby was good at maths, Tessa languages, and Kate games.
f) Girls can, and must, be provided with the same educational opportunities as boys are.
g) We believed in, and fought for, the right to educate our children.

2
Suggested answer:
a) My primary school days had not been very happy and nor were my secondary school days. For a start, my teachers didn't seem as concerned for me as they were for the other children. Nor did I devote as much time to my studies as I should have done, perhaps. But more than that, I had the feeling that if I was developing as a human being I was doing so not because of, but in spite of, what they were trying to knock into me. In short, I thought it was a waste of time. I wish now that I had said so then.
b) Because of these unhappy memories of my schooling (and because my wife had similar memories of hers) we decided that we would educate our own children at home. To do so, naturally, required a radical reorganization of our daily routine. Had we not done so, the children would have been left largely to their own devices. I arranged to work mainly afternoons and Sharon mainly evenings. This way we had the mornings entirely free. A neighbour was keen to have her children join ours, giving us six in all. I dedicated myself to the younger boys and girls and Sharon to the older ones.

VOCABULARY

1
a) 1   2   3   4   5   6   7
b) 5   6
c) 5   6   7
d) 1   3   6   7
e) 4   5   7
f) 1   2   4   6   7
g) 1   2   3   6   7

2
b) We came up against unexpected difficulties with the project and had to abandon it.
c) Josh is in trouble again: that boy finds it impossible to keep out of mischief.
d) Forgive me for forgetting your birthday. I promise I'll make up for it.
e) The TV that was stolen was insured so I'm going to put in for £500.
f) Some people think they can get away with murder, but we intend to prove that crime does not pay.
g) How long do you think you can put up with that dog barking downstairs?
h) This government is not going to give in to pressure. We will stand up to both the unions and the bosses.
i) She got off to a bad start but by the end of the race she had nearly caught up with the winner.
j) The new housing scheme comes up for review next month, so we will have a better idea as to how it has been working.

READING

1

Mary liked school, Molly didn't. Mary did well academically, Molly didn't.

2

a) 'I was a different kind of animal to them, having grown as old as I had in that very isolated way.'

b) She had teachers, not nuns.

c) Convent; the Loreto order; the nuns; the Reverend Mother

d) She had a certain liking for it, and loved Tennyson and Kipling.

e) She went to a day school; she was not forced to study at home.

f) There wasn't a great intellectual stimulus at home.

3

a) upbringing   b) ghastly   c) régime   d) naughty
e) gregarious   f) readily   g) all-rounder   h) have no qualms   i) cooped up

4

a) ii   b) ii   c) i

LANGUAGE PATTERNS

b) He was not bright enough to go to university.

c) Brian was not tall enough to be policeman.

d) She was not motivated enough to succeed.

e) He considered that the children were not disciplined enough.

f) You are not old enough to go to school.

g) You are not qualified enough for this job.

WRITING

Education is an experience we all share. Everyone at some time or other has been to school. Like work, like marriage, it is a universal human experience. There are few of us who, when reminiscences of schooldays start to flow, can't contribute a tale of our own. They are not always happy stories. They are quite often harrowing. *Nevertheless*, they have a strong attraction. Was X – now a company director – beaten as a child? Wasn't Y – permanently sedated these days – once top of her class? As Wordsworth wrote: 'The child is father of the man'. Our school stories tell us not just where we've been, but who we are.

Unit 15

READING

The text is a manifesto.

1

Energy; Clean seas; Rainforests; Genetic engineering

2

a) ... This must happen because the polluting emissions from burning fossil fuels are poisoning the atmosphere and threatening to wreck the world's climate patterns. *How, and how quickly, can the world wean itself from fossil fuels?* This is the central challenge posed by global warming and all atmospheric pollution.

b) ... This means ending all discharges of chemical waste and oil directly or indirectly into the sea. *This in turn means an end to all discharges into rivers, sewers and into the atmosphere.* Greenpeace will also campaign ...

c) The Greenpeace approach to rainforest campaigning will, as a priority, be led by Greenpeace offices which have been established within countries which host the rainforests. *One of our aims is to provide rainforest campaigns within these countries with the kind of resources and expertise developed and enjoyed in the rich countries where Greenpeace grew up.* It is crucial to stop the destruction of the forests...

d) Now, by genetic manipulation, totally contrived species of plants and animals can be created and sustained in what may become very productive but largely artificial and highly simplified environments. *This process in effect reverses natural evolution, which tends towards diversity.* Greenpeace is fundamentally opposed....

3

a) False   b) True   c) False   d) True   e) True
f) False   g) True

4

a) wreck   b) wean itself   c) paramount   d) thrive
e) ban   f) globe   g) compounded   h) myriad
i) vast tracts   j) undermine   k) patenting   l) versed

5

a) mounting   b) fundamentally   c) deeply
d) laying   e) drawing   f) tackle

TALKING EFFECTIVELY

1

environ<u>men</u>tal
evo<u>lu</u>tion
i<u>mag</u>inative
<u>at</u>mosphere
eco<u>log</u>ical
pri<u>or</u>ity
de<u>vel</u>oped
<u>eq</u>uity
di<u>ver</u>sity
agri<u>cul</u>tural
<u>hab</u>itats
manipu<u>la</u>tion
ge<u>net</u>ic
engi<u>nee</u>ring

2

en<u>vi</u>ronment (different)
e<u>volve</u> (different)
imagi<u>na</u>tion (different)
atmo<u>spher</u>ic (different)
e<u>col</u>ogy (different)
pri<u>or</u>itise (same)
de<u>vel</u>opment (same)
<u>eq</u>uitable (same)
di<u>verse</u> (same)
<u>ag</u>riculture (different)
<u>hab</u>itable (same)
ma<u>nip</u>ulative (different)
ge<u>net</u>icist (same)
engi<u>neer</u> (same)

LEARNING GRAMMAR

1
b) mixed   c) mixed   d) pure (2)   e) pure (2)
f) pure (sometimes called type 0)   g) pure (3)
h) pure (1)   i) mixed   j) pure (2)   k) mixed
l) mixed

2
a) are not   b) had not mounted   c) is; will   d) will
continue; will continue   e) accepts; will be
f) weren't; would have been   g) had not fallen; would
be

3
a) had seen   b) had   c) played   d) had survived
e) rose   f) had known   g) live   h) lived   i) lived

LANGUAGE PATTERNS

a) Greenpeace recommends that all nuclear power
   plants (should) be closed.
b) It is vital that the oceans be cleaned up.
c) It is essential to protect the rainforests.
d) Greenpeace proposes that deep-sea mining be
   banned.
e) They insist on the rich nations reducing their energy
   needs.
f) Greenpeace recommends that dependence on fossil
   fuels be reduced.

LISTENING

	Main worry	Personal contribution
1	Destruction of wildlife at sea	Only eats 'dolphin friendly' tuna
2	Polluted beaches	
3	Destruction of ozone layer	Doesn't buy CFC aerosols Uses unleaded petrol
4	Chopping down too many trees	Saves paper for recycling Uses recycled paper

WRITING

1 Topic sentences	4		6		9	
2 Comment sentences	7	3	8	2	1	5

3 Sentence order: 4 7 3 9 1 5 6 8 2

Unit 16

READING

1
a) True   b) True   c) False   d) True   e) True
f) False   g) True   h) True   i) True

2
a) childbirth   b) engineering   c) a recurring disease

3
a) sketchy   b) at loggerheads   c) gave vent to
d) recurring   e) wrestling   f) tussles   g) irrevocable

h) oxywelding   i) flimsy   j) drove (them) to
distraction

LANGUAGE PATTERNS

b) Fresh fruit is good to eat.
c) You are difficult to work with.
d) Phrasal verbs are not easy to learn.
e) The holiday was painful to remember.
f) She was a pleasure to share a flat with.
g) Her lecture was difficult to follow.
h) He is pleasant to talk to.
i) A car is a headache to own.

LEARNING GRAMMAR

1
a) 3   b) 4   c) 1   d) 2   e) 5

2
a) had phoned   b) would answer   c) visited   d) will
be   e) liked   f) like   g) had   h) drove

3
b) I wish I hadn't lost my address book!
c) I wish he would keep quiet!
d) I wish I had a video!
e) Will it rain? I wish it would!
f) I wish I could type!
g) I wish I hadn't failed the entrance test!
h) I wish you hadn't lied to me!
i) I wish I wasn't so fat!

VOCABULARY

a) telling   b) tell   c) tell   d) story   e) story
f) tale   g) story   h) tell

WRITING

Patrick White's great-grandfather went from England to
Australia in 1826, and the family has remained there. Mr
White was born in England in 1912, when his parents
were in Europe for two years. At six months he was
taken back to Australia where his father owned a sheep
station. When he was thirteen he was sent to school in
England, to Cheltenham, where, in his words, 'It was
understood the climate would be temperate and a
colonial acceptable.' Neither proved true, and after four
rather miserable years there he went to King's College,
Cambridge, where he specialized in languages. After
leaving the university he settled in London, determined
to become a writer. His novel *Happy Valley* was
published in 1939; *The Living and the Dead* in 1941.
Then during the war he was an RAF Intelligence officer in
the Middle East and Greece.

Unit 17

READING

1
b

2
a) 5   b) 2   c) 6   d) 1   e) 3   f) 4

3

a) quarter-century   b) blank out   c) I give all that the cold shoulder   d) swearing   e) the public prints (poetical language)   f) to take in

4

a

5

a

LEARNING GRAMMAR

1

a) It all happened when I was much younger.
b) I was the happiest person in all the world.
c) Pierre is as intelligent as me.
d) People don't work as hard as they think.
e) He looks younger than he really is.
f) There are worse things that could happen to you if you drink.
g) She is a worse student than me and she is the fastest runner of all the girls in the class.
h) I'm much more tired on holiday than at work.

2

b) My memory is getting worse and worse.
c) Our English class is getting better and better.
d) These exercises are getting more and more difficult.
e) Grammar is getting more and more interesting.
f) The boys are getting more and more good-looking. or ... better and better looking.
g) Our employees are getting more and more well-paid. or ... better and better paid.

3

b) 'How short do you want your hair?' 'Very short. In fact, the shorter the better.'
c) 'Which strawberries shall I buy?' 'The cheap ones. In fact the cheaper the better.'
d) 'How far away shall I bury the rubbish?' 'The further the better.'
e) 'I'm going away for a long time!' 'Good. The longer the better.'
f) 'How many people shall we invite?' 'As many as possible. The more the better.' or '... the more the merrier.'
g) 'I'll take you out to eat – somewhere expensive.' 'Oh good. The more expensive the better.'

4

1 getting   2 harmful   3 likely   4 better   5 such
6 performed   7 in   8 as   9 as   10 still
11 kinder   12 more

5

a) worse   b) more welcome   c) smaller   d) nearer
e) farther   f) shorter   g) more careless   h) higher

a) 7   b) 4   c) 5   d) 6   e) 3   f) 8   g) 2   h) 1

LANGUAGE PATTERNS

As I get older, I get more and more *like* my father. Although I'm not *as* bald *as* he was in his old age, I'm starting to lose my hair, and, *as* he always used to say, 'The fewer, the wiser.' It often seems to me *as* if children start to look more *like* their parents the more they start to understand them. My father and I used to fight *like* cat and dog, especially in the days when I was working *as* a singer in a band and looked *as* if I didn't have a penny to my name. In those days, few people realised we were related. Nowadays, *as* I said before, we grow more and more *like* each other, both in outlook and appearance.

VOCABULARY

b) as light as a feather   c) as old as the hills   d) as regular as clockwork   e) as good as gold   f) as sober as a judge   g) as mad as a hatter   h) as fresh as a daisy   i) as cool as a cucumber   j) as blind as a bat

LISTENING

	What they fear	What they look forward to	How they hope to stay young
1	Not being able to get around	Giving opinions more freely	Rowing to keep fit
2	Being dependent on others	Freedom to please yourself	Physical exercise Having adventures
3	Feeling of worthless-ness	Feeling of serenity	Running
4	Losing physical strength	Chance to do all the things you've always wanted to	Keeping busy

WRITING

Suggested answer
Medical advances may mean that one day we could live forever. That is the conclusion researchers in the USA have reached after a study of the humble fruit fly.

After studying a million flies, they found that their chances of dying, rather than increasing in old age, seem to level off. This contradicts previously held views on ageing. It may mean that there is no genetically defined limit to the fruit fly's life.

And if this is the case with humans, it might mean we could live forever! (88 words)

Unit 18

VOCABULARY

a) 3   b) 9   c) 7   d) 8   e) 6   f) 1   g) 2   h) 5   i) 4

READING

1 c   **2** a   **3** b   **4** c   **5** c   **6** b   **7** a   **8** b   **9** a
10 a) iii   b) i   c) ii   d) i   e) iii   f) ii   g) i   h) iii

LEARNING GRAMMAR

Focussing on information: auxiliary verbs

1

a) I've never had squid but I *have* had octopus.
b) I never saw *The Birds* but I did see *Psycho*.
c) I don't like Handel but I do like Purcell.
d) He can't play very well, but he *can* sing beautifully.
e) 'You haven't cleaned your teeth.' 'I *have* cleaned them'
f) 'You didn't do your homework.' 'I did do it.'

2

b) I don't like some things about New York but I do like my apartment.
c) I don't worship success but I do believe in hard work.
d) We didn't change the world but we did change people's attitudes.
e) She doesn't look like her mother but she does have some of her mother's character.
f) We didn't go to Macy's but we did go to Bloomingdales.
g) He doesn't do any cleaning but he does do the dishes.

Focussing on information: cleft sentences

1

b) It was in 1492 that Columbus discovered America.
c) It was John Wilkes Booth who shot Lincoln.
d) It was St Paul's Cathedral that Wren designed.
e) It was in Zurich that Joyce wrote *Ulysses*.
f) It was Visconti who made a film of *Death in Venice*.
g) What Isabel Burton did was burn her husband's diaries.
h) It was in Tahiti that Gauguin died.
i) What Verdi did was write an opera about Othello.
j) It was in 1924 that Kafka died.

2

b) He can't drive so what he does is walk everywhere.
c) I can't read small print so what I do is use a magnifying glass.
d) I used to have trouble learning vocabulary so what I do is keep a notebook of new words.
e) She couldn't get to sleep so what she did was make herself a hot drink.
f) His job is very stressful so what he does is do yoga.
g) She couldn't find a novel she liked so what she did was write one herself.
h) It was after midnight so what he did was take a taxi.

3

A: And you stayed with Margaret?
B: No, it was Helen who we stayed with.
A: And you bought a car, didn't you?
B: No, what we did was hire a car.
A: And Gary had an accident, I gather?
B: No, it was me who had the accident.
A: And you went skiing in the mountains?
B: No, what we did was go walking in the mountains.
A: And you came back last Tuesday, right?
B: No, it was Monday when we came back.

TALKING EFFECTIVELY

Question tags

a) Fall   b) Rise   c) Rise   d) Fall   e) Fall   f) Rise
g) Fall   h) Rise   i) Fall   j) Rise

Sentence stress

1 June   2 we   3 engaged   4 Tom   5 Evelyn
6 was

LANGUAGE PATTERNS

a) Whenever he phones, I'm in the bath.
b) No matter what I did, I couldn't open the window.

c) However much I practise, my Spanish never seems to improve.
d) Whenever I go shopping, I buy something I don't need.
e) However much I try, I can never a finish a novel by Henry James. or However hard I try …
f) Whichever way we go, there's no exit.

WRITING

Suggested answer:
One day Djuha bought three kilos of lamb's meat in the market and took it home to his wife. After explaining to her how he would like to have it prepared for his dinner, he went out again.

Djuha's wife seasoned the meat and cooked it carefully. But it smelled so delicious that she sent for her brother and the two of them feasted on it until nothing was left.

When Djuha came home and asked for his dinner, his wife wailed, 'While I was busy in the kitchen the cat ran in and ate up the meat, and now I have nothing to give you for dinner.'

Djuha grabbed the cat and set it on the scale, which tipped at exactly three kilos. 'If this is the meat,' said Djuha, 'then where is the cat? And if this is the cat, then tell me where is the meat?'

1 Read the extract from the story and write *T* (for *True*) or *F* (for *False*) next to these statements.

a) The children's father was no longer living with them. ☐

b) The mother did not have much money. ☐

c) Their father would bring them presents on New Year's Eve. ☐

d) The mother claimed a special relationship with Father Christmas in order to persuade the boys that Father Christmas was true. ☐

2 Match each child in column A with an adjective in column B.

A		**B**	
a)	Billy	1	retarded
b)	Joshua	2	fearful
c)	Jason	3	bright
d)	Ben	4	suspicious

3 What clues in the story suggest that Ruby was at times:

a) over-worked? _____

_____

b) ingenious? _____

_____

c) irresponsible? _____

_____

d) bored? _____

_____

e) hard up? _____

_____

c) us/the bank/a loan/had offered

_____

d) my husband and me/had lent/they/£5000

_____

e) cost/it/us/a lot

_____

f) the bank/we/owe/£1000

_____

g) will send/them/it/to/we

_____

2 How many sentences can you make out of these elements?

a) Ted/Todd/lent/£5 _____

_____

b) gave/the woman/the man/a flower _____

_____

_____

c) the priest/the youth/the dragon/to/offered ____

_____

_____

_____

_____

_____

_____

d) sent/her/they/him/to _____

_____

e) the prince/the princess/the frog/showed _____

_____

_____

_____

LANGUAGE PATTERNS

Verbs with two objects

1 Put the words below in the correct order to make sentences.

a) the bank manager/to/a letter/has written/me

_____

b) the letter/I/to/showed/my husband

_____

LEARNING GRAMMAR

Contrast

1 Underline the correct alternative in these sentences.

a) *Whereas/Although* it was late, they started working.

b) The book was difficult. I enjoyed it *though/although*.

c) The book was difficult. *Still/Though*, I enjoyed it.

d) The Indian elephant has small ears, *whereas/ though* the African elephant has large ears.

e) *While/However* we didn't see any elephants, we did see some giraffes.

f) *While/Whereas* I like elephants, I prefer giraffes.

g) *Though/Whereas* they are strictly protected, hunting of elephants continues.

h) Elephants are strictly protected. *However/ Although*, hunting continues.

2 In each of these three texts, one word fits all the spaces. Choose the missing word for each text from the box below.

whereas however although still
though yet while

a) _____ Damien and Agnes were young when they married, they didn't have their first child until well into their thirties. They preferred to live as _____ they weren't really married at all. Their social life was a constant round of parties and socialising. This all changed when Flo was born, _____ . Tiny _____ she was, she closed the door on their youth forever.

b) _____ never very healthy, Flo grew rapidly. Her parents, _____ it took them time to get used to the new arrival, were devoted. _____ Damien was working in his studio, Agnes would spend every waking moment with the child. Damien would take over in the evenings, _____ Agnes worked at her dissertation.

c) _____ , they managed to retain a vestige of their previously wild social life. Agnes _____ attended her regular poetry readings, and Damien was _____ a conspicuous figure at gallery openings. But as Flo's health deteriorated _____ further, they were seen less and less in 'society'. ' _____ ,' said Agnes, 'what does society count, compared to the health of a child?'

WRITING

Cohesion: additions and contrasts

1 In the following text, underline the correct linking expression from the alternatives.

 (*Although/However*) women have been making up more than half the intake on law courses in recent years, only 23 per cent of practising solicitors are female. (*And/On the other hand*) the higher you get in the judiciary, the more unbalanced the figures become. At the very top of the legal profession are the 10 judges who form the highest court of appeal in the land. Not one is a woman (*however/moreover*).

The picture is much the same in the medical profession. (*Despite the fact that/On the one hand*) almost half of all students entering medical and dentistry school in recent years have been women, only 23 per cent of all practising doctors and dentists are women. (*Whereas/On the other hand*), 80 per cent of nurses and 83 per cent of midwives are female. (*Besides/Again*), the higher the position, the fewer women you'll find. There are 1045 general surgeons in England and Wales (*but/however*) only eleven are women.

(*And/Also*) what about teachers? Sixty-one per cent of today's teachers are female, (*though/yet*) this figure does not extend to head posts - only 43 per cent of head teachers are female. (*Moreover/Conversely*) at Oxford and Cambridge, (*despite/even though*) over 40 per cent of their undergraduates are female, only one in seven full-time academics is a woman.

(adapted from *Essentials*)

2 Mini Sagas

Reorganise this fifty word mini saga by putting the sentences in the right order.

(1) 'My son!' (2) Now, how could this be? (3) Harold and son took their places next day in the courtroom. (4) The would-be mugger was repentant. (5) Coming home late down a back-street, Harold felt a knife in his kidneys. (6) 'My son!' cried the judge, on entering. (7) Turning to face his assailant, he gasped.

Now, can you solve the puzzle?

Living in colour

VOCABULARY

Colour

1   Underline the odd one out in each group.

a) <u>glow</u>   shadow   darkness   gloom

b) tone   brightness   shade   hue

c) dim   dull   hazy   dazzling

d) paint   palette   pigment   dye

e) scarlet   emerald   red   crimson

f) colourful   faded   bright   vivid

g) shine   fade   glitter   brighten

2   Choose a word from each set in Exercise 1 to complete the relevant sentences.

a) The tree cast a long _____ across the garden.

b) Do you have this colour in a darker _____?

c) It was an overcast and _____ winter's day.

d) Do not wash this garment in hot water or the _____ will run.

e) She's got blue eyes and _____ hair.

f) He was wearing an old T-shirt and _____ blue jeans.

g) 'All that _____ is not gold.'

READING

1   Read the text opposite and tick the title you think is most appropriate.

a) The Influence of Turner ☐

b) The Art of the Grey ☐

c) Matisse Discovers The Open Air ☐

d) Matisse's Travels ☐

e) The Apprenticeship Years ☐

(from *Matisse* by Gérard Durozoi)

2   Now put these events in chronological order.

a) He went to Corsica. ☐

b) He visited the National Gallery. ☐

c) He met Pissarro. ☐

d) He paid tribute to Turner. ☐

e) He went to Toulouse. ☐

f) He married Amélie. ☐

g) He went to Brittany. ☐

During the years of his apprenticeship, Matisse developed an intense curiosity for all the models that painting could offer him. He made copies at the Louvre, and acquired amongst his colleagues a reputation as a "scholar of the art of the greys". Then, in 1895, Matisse spent the summer working in Brittany. From that point on the Louvre was seen in contradistinction to the open air favoured by the Impressionists, and Matisse's palette began tentatively to brighten.

In 1898, Matisse married Amélie Parayre, originally from Toulouse, and the young couple left for London on honeymoon. On the advice of Camille Pissarro, whom he had met the previous year, Matisse made a point of visiting the National Gallery, to see the Turners there. The romantic tributes that Matisse paid to Turner in old age leave no doubt that the pictures impressed him deeply. He placed them as "the passage between tradition and Impressionism". The question of this "passage" (between the Louvre and the open air) preoccupied him a great deal, and gave him increasing cause for thought after the spring of 1898 when he travelled to Corsica (where his sister-in-law lived), and to Toulouse (staying with his parents-in-law) and was overcome by the violent splendour of natural light, fascinated, as a "man from the north", with the special qualities of the Mediterranean; "It was in Ajaccio that I first began to marvel at the south." The small paintings produced in Corsica and in the weeks that followed bear witness to this "wonder" with a violent rush of bright colour, not always under control, but constantly asserting the wish to break with the "art of the grey" in order to achieve a new conception of light, with the help of the open air.

3 Write *T* (for *True*) or *F* (for *False*) next to the following statements.

a) The summer in Brittany marked a major change in his development. ☐

b) Matisse met Turner in his old age. ☐

c) Pissarro advised Matisse to look at the Turners. ☐

d) He stayed with Amélie's parents in Toulouse. ☐

e) Matisse had no wish to break with 'the art of the grey'. ☐

5 Match the two halves of these compound colour adjectives.

A		**B**
a)	emerald	1 -pink
b)	lemon	2 -grey
c)	sky	3 -green
d)	salmon	4 -black
e)	jet	5 -red
f)	steel	6 -yellow
g)	blood	7 -blue

4 Read this description of one of Matisse's most famous paintings. Mark the colours onto the black-and-white copy.

from *Matisse: The Masterworks* by Gérard Durozoi

Nothing could be less substantial than the ragged patches of emerald and scarlet that serve for human figures in *Intérieur à Collioure*. A perfect harmony of red, blue-green and pink, this interior scene uses materials sparsely, occasionally allowing the texture of the canvas to show through. Its subject is a siesta in a bedroom flooded with reflected light. The light enters the room through the window, but the bright blue-green walls are also invested with light. The green figure sprawling on pink seems to abandon herself to the colour. Against the orange balcony the red of the girl's dress seems a different red from that of the floor in the foreground. They are in fact exactly the same colour.

LISTENING

Healing with colour

1 [📼 11.1] What effects do different colours have on people? Match the colour in column A with its characteristic effect in column B.

A	B
a) green	1 calming
b) red	2 conducive to working
c) blue	3 promotes healing
d) orange	4 conducive to thinking
e) yellow	5 stimulating

Now, listen to the first part of this interview with colour therapist Ivor Crystal and see if you were right.

2 Listen to Part Two of the interview and fill in the chart.

Colour	Food	Good for (illness)

LEARNING GRAMMAR

It

1 Complete the following paragraph with *it* or *this*.

Critical acceptance of Matisse has fluctuated over the years. ¹_____ is in part due to shifts in fashion. ²_____ comes as some surprise to discover that, when he first exhibited, the art-ist and ugly. ³_____ contrasts with the later view of Matisse as being a somewhat facile and decorative artist. Or worse, that he was a lightweight who, unlike Picasso, never made a single political statement in his art. ⁴_____ is partly Matisse's own fault: his best known remark is that he wanted 'an art of balance, of purity and serenity.' Ever since, some critics have found ⁵_____ hard to forgive, even as they began to re-instate him as one of the century's most avant-garde artists. ⁶_____ was a view that started to take root in the sixties, and ⁷_____ derives principally from an appeciation of his later work. Above all ⁸_____ is as a colorist that Matisse is chiefly remembered. ⁹_____ is why ¹⁰_____ is often claimed that Matisse was not a figurative painter at all, but that he belonged entirely to an abstract tradition. The current exhibition at the Museum of Modern Art exposes ¹¹_____ as yet another misconception in a long history of misconceptions. ¹²_____ will be interesting to see what new turns Matisse's critical fortunes take.

2 Rewrite the following sentences, using *it*.

a) Doing these exercises is fun.
   It's fun doing these exercises.

b) That carrots are good for you is obvious.
   _____

c) Different colours affect me. It's funny.
   _____

d) Whether colours have healing properties is doubtful.
   _____
   _____

e) People heal faster in green rooms. It's extraordinary.
   _____
   _____

f) That some colours are stimulating is possible.
   _____
   _____

g) Eating an all-yellow meal would be strange.
   _____
   _____

h) That prunes help you sleep is unlikely.

_____

i) Some people find colour therapy hard to believe. That's not surprising.

_____

LANGUAGE PATTERNS

Verbs followed by *it*

Rewrite the following passage in your notebook, by adding or removing *it* where necessary.

After ten months at Innisfree I find hard to believe what was like living in the city. Is now evening and I sit watching the linnets as the sunlight it fades. How I love when the thin crescent of the moon it hangs above the lake: it is a sight I will never forget it. I hope I will never grow tired of it: I think unlikely. I have never experienced such peace and happiness. I owe all to my decision that day nearly a year ago when, standing on the grey city pavement, I found suddenly unbearable and resolved to leave at once. Now, looking back, I wonder how I put up with for so long.

TALKING EFFECTIVELY

/ əʊ /

[🖭 11.2] Underline the /əʊ/ sounds in this poem and then listen to the recording to check.

I will arise and go (= / əʊ /) now, and go to Innisfree,
And a small cabin build there, of clay and wattles made:
Nine bean-rows shall I have there, and a hive for the honey bee,
And live alone in the bee-loud glade.

And I shall have some peace there, for peace comes dropping slow,
Dropping from the veils of the morning to where the cricket sings;
There midnight's all a glimmer, and noon a purple glow,
And evening full of the linnet's wings.

I will arise and go now, for always night and day
I hear lake water lapping with low sounds by the shore;
While I stand on the roadway, or on the pavements grey
I hear it in the deep heart's core.

(from *The Lake Isle of Innisfree* by W.B. Yeats)

Can you identify four different ways of spelling the /əʊ/ sound? _____

Now read the poem aloud.

WRITING

Read this biography of the poet W.B. Yeats. Reduce it to about 75 words, using grammatically complete sentences, and retaining the main facts. Rewrite it in your notebook.

William Butler Yeats was born in Ireland in 1865, the son of J.B. Yeats, and the brother of Jack Yeats, both of whom were celebrated painters. Yeats, too, studied painting, and it was while he was a student at the school of Art in Dublin that he developed a fascination for mystic religion and the occult. He was also deeply interested in Irish myths and legends, and he soon became a leader of what was known as the Irish literary renaissance, one of whose aims was to revive ancient Irish folklore. He lived much of his life in Sligo, where many of his poems are set. His early poems, including *The Wanderings of Oison* (1889), combine an interest in Symbolism with an intense nationalism. This was fuelled by his hopeless but impassioned love for the revolutionary patriot Maud Gonne. Verses from this period include "The Lake Isle of Innisfree" (see above) and "When You Are Old". With Lady Gregory and others he helped establish the Irish National theatre in 1898 (later based at the Abbey Theatre), where many of his plays were first performed, including *The Countess Cathleen* (1892), which contributed to an Irish revival in the theatre. As well as writing poetry and drama, Yeats turned his hand to prose: the stories collected in *The Celtic Twilight* (1893) draw heavily on folkloric themes. As he grew older, Yeats's poetry became simpler and more lyrical, as he moved away from mysticism towards a greater realism, and a simpler, more colloquial style. His later volumes such as *Michael Robartes and the Dancer* (1921) and *The Tower* (1928) contain some of the greatest 20th century verse in English. In 1917 Yeats married Georgie Hyde-Lees, whose interest in the occult influenced his later work. Yeats served as a senator of the Irish Free State (1922 – 8) and was awarded the Nobel Prize for Literature in 1923. He died in Ireland in 1939.

The quality of animal life

▼

VOCABULARY

Expressions: animal names

1 Match the two halves of these animal expressions and then see if you can work out their meaning.

A	**B**
a) to look a gift horse	1 with one stone
b) to let the cat	2 that laid the golden egg
c) to kill the goose	3 before they hatch
d) to take the bull	4 in the mouth
e) to kill two birds	5 by the horns
f) to count your chickens	6 out of the bag

2 Now use one of them to fill in the gap in each of the three following stories.

a) I was working too hard for too little money. One day I had had enough. I decided

_____ and

walked straight into the boss's office and demanded a salary rise. He looked startled for a moment and then just said: 'Well, how much do you want?'

b) Ben wanted an animal around the house, and I was a bit worried about burglars, so we

decided _____

and get a dog.

c) Nobody was supposed to know about our

engagement yet, but Sarah _____

_____ by telling Bill who is such a loudmouth, and of course he went and told everyone.

READING

One argument against the maltreatment of animals is that animals are capable of 'human-like' feelings – not just of pain, but of such 'higher order' emotions as grief, compassion and selflessness.

1   Read this extract. Before you read, answer these questions.

a) What is the plural of *goose*? _____

b) What is a male goose called? _____

c) What is a young goose called? _____

d) What noise does a goose make? _____

Just Like an Animal

A bereaved goose was revived in quite an unexpected manner. It was one of a pair of geese, and a fox took the gander. His mate followed the fox for a quarter of a mile, as the tracks showed, then became bogged down in the mud. A neighbour living near the spot heard the persistent honking, went out to investigate, at 4.30 a.m., rescued the goose and returned it to its owner.

Geese, we know, mate for life. They epitomize, in the world of birds, marital fidelity. There are known instances in which one partner of a mated pair dies and the other calls continuously for days on end. Here, then if anywhere, we ought to expect some indication of grief at the loss of a partner. Geese also gave us our first insight into the phenomenon of imprinting. When a gosling hatches it becomes imprinted on the first thing it sees. This would normally be its parents. These it follows around, so imprinting is a natural method of keeping the young with their parents. If, however, its eyes first beheld a person, the gosling would tend to follow that person around as if tied to him by an invisible thread. A gosling has also been known to become imprinted on a wheelbarrow, the first object it saw after hatching. It rested beside it and followed it when the wheelbarrow was being used.

It so happened that the adult goose in our story, when it was returned to its owner, was placed on the ground beside a wheelbarrow. She became imprinted. Except when grazing, she spent all her time sitting beside it. Anyone approaching the wheelbarrow was treated to an aggressive display, as the goose would have done had she had her partner with her. The goose "talked" to the wheelbarrow before going off to graze. When someone took the wheelbarrow away, in the normal course of using it, the goose would follow honking and hissing, until the wheelbarrow was left stationary. There were occasions when the wheelbarrow had to be taken well away, out of sight of the goose. Then she would seek the company of the rear wheel of the car parked near the house.

(from *Just Like an Animal* by Maurice Burton)

---

2   Answer these questions.

a) Which of these events did *not* happen? Put a cross (X) in the appropriate boxes.

   i) The goose's partner was taken by a fox. ☐

   ii) The goose tried to follow it. ☐

   iii) The goose died of grief. ☐

   iv) A neighbour discovered the goose and *True.* returned it. ☐

   v) The goose transferred her affection to a wheelbarrow. ☐

   vi) The goose treated the wheelbarrow aggressively. ☐

   vii) A car wheel took the place of the wheelbarrow in its absence. ☐

b) Which of these statements are true? Write *T* in the appropriate boxes.

   i) Geese have only one partner all their lives. ☐

   ii) Surprisingly, geese do not show grief at the loss of a partner. ☐

   iii) Parent geese follow their young around. ☐

   iv) If at birth a baby goose sees a person, it might follow that person around. ☐

   v) Baby geese have been known to follow wheelbarrows. ☐

3   'A bereaved goose was revived in quite an unexpected manner'. What was the 'unexpected manner'?

a) A neighbour rescued it. ☐

b) It transferred its affection to a wheelbarrow. ☐

c) It transferred its affection to a person. ☐

d) It called continuously for days on end. ☐

4   What is the writer's objective in telling this story?

a) To show how stupid geese are. ☐

b) To show how much geese suffer. ☐

c) To show how a goose dealt with its grief. ☐

d) To show how faithful geese are. ☐

5 Find a word, or expression, in the text that means:

Paragraph 1:

a) deprived, by death, of a relation _____

b) got stuck _____

c) particular place _____

d) continuous _____

Paragraph 2:

e) represent _____

f) faithfulness _____

g) saw _____

h) emerging from an egg _____

Paragraph 3:

i) feeding on grass, etc. _____

j) not moving _____

LANGUAGE PATTERNS

Participle clauses

'*Anyone approaching the wheelbarrow* was treated to an aggressive display...'

This is an example of a participle clause used to identify who you are talking about. These clauses always follow the noun or pronoun they refer to.
  Rewrite these sentences, using participle clauses.

a) If people wanted to smoke they had to sit at the back.
  People wanting to smoke had to sit at the back.

b) Anyone who supposes that this story is invented doesn't know much about animals.

_____

_____

c) Take the case of a person who is drowning.

_____

d) If anyone tried to touch her kittens, they would be attacked.

_____

_____

e) Geese that live in the wild seldom experience this problem.

_____

_____

f) If anyone hears of a similar case, please let me know.

_____

_____

g) The dog bit the woman who was maltreating it.

_____

h) Any animal that lives with humans will think that it is human too.

_____

_____

i) Have you ever heard of a goose that followed a lawnmower around?

_____

_____

LEARNING GRAMMAR

Nouns in groups

1 Complete these sentences by choosing the correct combination of nouns.

a) (*soup/bowl*) There are some Chinese *soupbowls* in the cupboard.
  I think I'll just have a *bowl of soup* for dinner.

b) (*match/box*) A packet of cigarettes and a _____, please.

c) (*tea/cup*) What I like after work is a nice _____.

d) (*mail/bag*) The prisoners spent every day making _____.

e) (*match/box*) She kept her contact lenses in a _____.

f) (*wine/bottle*) I think we should take a _____ to the party.

g) (*wine/bottle*) In the centre of the table there was a _____ with a candle in it.

h) (*tea/cup*) For the sauce you'll need a _____ of flour.

2   Devise noun groups for these definitions.

a) a shop where you buy shoes
    a shoe shop

b) a trap for mice _____

c) an icecream made with strawberries

    _____

d) plants for indoors _____

e) a table for playing cards on _____

f) a note worth five pounds _____

g) a necklace made of pearls _____

h) the side of a road _____

i) a bed of flowers _____

j) a bottle containing two litres _____

k) the sun at midday _____

l) a week of forty hours _____

m) paste for teeth _____

3   Write headlines for these news items, using the clues provided.

a) man/kidnap/charged/drama
    A 37-year-old man will appear in court today
    on charges relating to the kidnap of a twenty-
    nine year old mother of two in Barchester last
    week.
    Kidnap drama man charged

b) death/probe/chase
    A Swindon woman has won a year-long fight
    for an official inquiry into the death of her
    husband in a high-speed chase with police.

    _____

c) man/cleared/case/bomb
    A man charged with blowing up the Allen
    County courthouse has had the charge
    dropped.

    _____

d) pit/riddle/threat/strike
    Union leaders yesterday denied that there was
    any substance to the story, printed in
    yesterday's Herald, of a threatened coal strike.
    'It is a complete mystery,' said Frederick Angas,
    speaking on behalf of the Union secretariat.

    _____

e) price/shock/bread/rise
    The Consumers' Association reports that
    shoppers have expressed 'anger and disbelief'
    on learning of the recent 13p rise in the cost of
    a loaf of bread.

    _____

4   Correct any errors in the following sentences.

a) There will be some world cup's boat races.

    _____

b) The course's fees are £900 for two months.

    _____

c) When we arrived at the airport the taxi of hotel
    wasn't there.

    _____

    _____

d) He stuck the explosives near the hinges of the
    safe's door.

    _____

    _____

e) One day he decided to leave his bachelor's life.

    _____

    _____

f) First I had to go to my friend house.

    _____

g) We also have a buses network.

    _____

h) I've got the house's key and I can return at
    night when I want.

    _____

    _____

WRITING

Headlines

> ## EYE DROPS OFF SHELVES
> Following warnings from the Food and Drug Administration, shopkeepers have been removing bottles of "WASHEX" eye-drops from their shelves, after it was discovered that they contained an hallucinogenic substance...

> ## Eye drops off shelves
> Readers at the Minneapolis City Library were shocked yesterday when a large blood-shot eye fell from the shelves of the reference section and then proceeded to make its way towards the periodicals. So far no one has claimed responsibility for the eye...

Which of the two news stories, A or B, is the real story – and which one is exploiting the ambiguity in the headline? _____

Look at these examples of headlines that have appeared in US newspapers. Each one is ambiguous; that is, it has an intended meaning, and an unintended meaning. Choose two, and write:

a) the (probable) *intended* opening paragraph, i.e., for the original article;

b) the *unintended* opening paragraph.

> ## Westinghouse Gives Robot Rights to Firm

> ## Johnson Teacher Talks Very Slow

> ## Late bus coordinator remembered

> ## French offer terrorist reward

(See the Key for an explanation of the ambiguities.)

How zany are you?

VOCABULARY

Multi-part verbs

With most transitive multi-part verbs, it is possible to put the object before or after the adverb particle (unless the object is a pronoun). For example:

He looked the word up in the dictionary.
(Or: *He looked up the word in the dictionary.*)

However there is a small class of multi-part verbs that, depending on their meaning, require that the adverb particle *always* follows the object. For example:

I'm sure I can bring my father round. = persuade him
(Not: *I'm sure I can bring round my father.*)

In the following sentences substitute the underlined verb phrase for a multi-part verb + object, using the prompt provided. In each case, decide if the particle can be separated or must be separated. Select the particle from the box below.

> forward   around   back (x2)   down
> up   apart

a) The sound of the ice-cream van <u>reminded Esther of</u> her childhood. (*take*)

_____

_____

b) They look so similar I can't <u>distinguish between</u> them. (*tell*)

_____

_____

c) Tony <u>failed to keep an appointment with</u> his girlfriend. (*stand*)

_____

_____

d) Why don't you <u>return</u> those bottles? (*take*)

_____

_____

e) Wayne is always <u>bullying</u> the other children. (*push*)

_____

_____

f) Let's <u>advance the date</u> of the meeting. (*bring*)

_____

_____

g) The doctor <u>attributed</u> my tiredness to lack of sleep. (*put*)

_____

_____

The unusual

1   Use a dictionary and put a tick in the table, according to whether these adjectives:

a) are colloquial/slang or not;
b) are normally applied only to people or to other things (e.g. films, clothes);
c) have a negative, rather than a neutral connotation.

	slang	people	things	negative
zany				
eccentric				
mad				
unconventional				
dotty				
weird				
crazy				
odd				
barmy				
obsessive				
insane				

2 Now put the following adjectives in order of severity, from not very severe to very severe.

crazy ☐ insane ☐ odd ☐
weird ☐ unconventional ☐
mad ☐

LISTENING

1 [📻 13.1] Listen to the interview with a clinical psychologist talking about a disease called OCD. Make notes about the interview by answering these questions.

a) What does OCD stand for?

_____

_____

b) What are the two main types of sufferers?

_____

_____

c) What often starts the disorder?

_____

_____

d) How many people are estimated to suffer from OCD in the USA?

_____

_____

e) What were the traditional forms of treatment?

_____

_____

f) Are drugs useless?

_____

_____

g) What form of treatment does the speaker recommend?

_____

_____

2 Use these notes to write a paragraph (of about 75 words) about OCD in your notebook.

READING

Read this text about a man with 'Obsessive-Compulsive Disorder', and answer the questions.

"For six years I sat in a chair doing nothing"

It is hard to believe that Ken Sell, a slim, animated 48-year-old British family man, was a 114-kilogram recluse 20 years ago.

"For six years I sat in a chair doing nothing, immersed with a contamination obsession," says Sell, who went out only five times, and in one year saw only seven people. The only time he got out of his chair was to sleep or go to the bathroom. "I was terrified of everything - blood, excrement, asbestos, fibreglass, radiation."

Sell became clinically depressed when he was 25. "I had relationship problems and was struggling to be a freelance comic-strip writer," he says. A trip to Canada triggered the disorder. "There was a drought and we couldn't wash often. I felt so dirty I held my hands away from my body. When I returned, suddenly I couldn't touch anything - total revulsion." Normal activities were impossible. "I ate with my fingers because I couldn't bear the idea of touching cutlery." His father made him a special table which no-one touched. Sell had an imaginary safe circle of about two metres in diameter around his body: if anyone invaded it he felt like he had been contaminated.

He washed his hands so often that the skin split and peeled, exposing his knuckle bones. He hardly ever walked anywhere, he developed ingrown toenails, and once hibernated in his bed for several weeks.

His compulsions were so strong that he had no time for anything else. "When you are handicapped you just focus on yourself," he says. "I engulfed my parents with the problem and did nothing myself. I got upset watching my father with his bad arthritis taking hours to change a fuse, something I could have done in five minutes, but instead I just sat there."

Sell tried every therapy available. "Doctors put me on heavy drugs and I sat in the chair singing to myself for 18 months. I refused a prefrontal lobotomy. No-one knew what was wrong, and no-one else suffered from it, apparently. They just took our money."

Sell's recovery happened quite by chance. Some Canadian relations arrived for a three-week stay, and he pretended to be well. "It was amazingly easy. I suddenly started living normally." The real test came, however, when a niece rifled through his cassette tapes: "I was desperately trying to remember which ones she had touched, and I said to myself, 'Oh, sod this. I can't keep a record of that, it's stupid.' "

As he recovered, his doctor suggested that he meet someone with a similar problem.

By 1980, Ken Sell and others had registered Phobic Action, a contact group for phobics and OCD sufferers. Today the director of Phobic Action, Sell admits that the Obsessive-Compulsive Disorder seems bogus, but denies that it is just indulgence. "You feel such a damn fool; half of you says you ought to snap out of it. OCD has no compassion, it takes as much space of your life as you allow it: if you don't fight, you begin to do less and less."

Sell is philosophical about the lost years; "It was one of those things; plenty of men lost a damn sight more in 1939-45." His mother destroyed the special table. ▬▬▬▬▬▬

(from *GH Magazine*)

1 Tick which of these are symptoms of OCD.

a) weight loss ☐   d) split skin ☐

b) clinical depression ☐   e) arthritis ☐

c) fear of contamination ☐ f) apathy ☐

2 Write *T* (for *True*) or *F* (for *False*) beside each statement.

a) The problem started during a trip to Canada. ☐

b) He ate with his fingers because he didn't like touching knives and forks. ☐

c) He had difficulty walking because of his toenails. ☐

d) He was upset because he couldn't help his father. ☐

e) He simulated normal behaviour when some relatives came to stay. ☐

f) He helped start Phobic Action. ☐

g) He regrets the years he lost. ☐

3 What evidence is there in the text that:

a) he is married with children?

_____

b) his parents were understanding?

_____

_____

c) he wanted to be cured?

_____

d) he distrusted his doctors' motives?

_____

_____

e) his family believe he is cured?

_____

4 Using the words in the box from the text, complete the following sentences.

```
revulsion   compulsion   compassion
indulgence
```

a) I'm not surprised you feel ill after a weekend of such _____.

b) Sometimes I get this _____ to start conversations with complete strangers.

c) I'm surprised he has chosen to be a nurse: he has never shown any _____ for the less fortunate.

d) I wish to complain about scenes of violence on television: they fill me with _____.

5 Using these words from the text, complete the following sentences.

```
obsessed   depressed   handicapped
```

a) Most mentally _____ people are capable of living normal lives.

b) The state of the environment _____ her to the point of despair.

c) Theories about Kennedy's assassination have _____ him for years. He's read everything there is to know on the subject.

6 Using these words from the text, complete the following sentences.

```
invaded   contaminated   engulfed   immersed
```

a) Don't drink the water. They say it has been _____.

b) He was so _____ in his book that he forgot to get off at his stop.

c) Our flat has been _____ by fleas.

d) She was completely _____ by the demands of her job and had no time for a life of her own.

LANGUAGE PATTERNS

Infinitives and -*ing* forms: review

Choose the correct form of the verb in these sentences from the text without (*to look/looking*)!

a) It is hard (*believing/to believe*) that Ken Sell, a slim, animated 48-year-old British family man, was a 114-kilogram recluse 20 years ago.

b) Some Canadian relations arrived for a three-week stay, and he pretended (*to be/being*) well.

c) 'It was amazingly easy. I suddenly started (*to live/living*) normally.'

d) 'I was desperately trying (*to remember/ remembering*) which ones she had touched.'

e) 'If you don't fight, you begin (*doing/to do*) less and less.'

Result clauses

'I felt so dirty [that] I held my hands away from my body.'
He washed his hands so often that the skin split and peeled.

The *that* clause is a result of something having an extreme quality (e.g. *dirty*), or being done in an extreme way (e.g. *often*). *So* is used with adjective and adverb phrases; *such* is used with noun phrases:

It was such a difficult job that he gave up.

So can be put at the head of the sentence. In this case, there is inversion of the subject and verb:

So obsessed was he with dirt that he scrubbed his hands to the bone.

Rewrite the following sentences, using the prompts provided:

a) The day was so hot we abandoned sightseeing.
It was _____

b) We walked out because the film was so offensive.
The film _____

c) She was so tired that she slept for fourteen hours.
So _____

d) There was such a crowd at the pool that we went home.
The pool was _____

e) The business was such a success they took on more staff.
So _____

f) The party was so noisy the police were called.
It was _____

LEARNING GRAMMAR

Cause, purpose, result

Rewrite the following sentences according to the prompts provided and so as to retain the meaning of the original as closely as possible.

a) The bridge collapsed because it had been badly designed.
Owing _____

b) She gave up work in order to look after her mother.
She gave up work so _____

c) Because of Ellen's flu, we've decided not to go out.
Since _____

d) We missed the train so we had to walk.
As a result of _____

e) Because it's raining they have taken a taxi.
They've taken a taxi on _____

f) You're a friend of mine, so I can tell you.
As _____

g) He drank. That's why she left him.
Because of _____

Linking ideas: defining and non-defining relative clauses

Complete these sentences by adding a relative pronoun.

a) That's the shop _____ I buy my muesli.

b) Those teachers _____ pupils are sitting exams tomorrow can have the day off.

c) The politician after _____ this street was named was a socialist.

d) I ran into Emma, _____ is looking very well.

e) It was four in the morning _____ he phoned.

f) The minister to _____ the question had been addressed refused to answer.

g) The son, in _____ name the car was registered, decided to sell it.

h) The house in _____ we grew up has been pulled down.

i) The house _____ we grew up has been pulled down.

j) It was a difficult time for Sell, _____ was being treated for depression.

k) It started on a visit to Canada, _____ , because of a drought, there was a water shortage.

l) He suffered from OCD for six years, during _____ time he hardly ever left his room.

TALKING EFFECTIVELY

Defining and non-defining clauses

[📼 13.2] Listen to the recording and identify which of the following (unpunctuated) sentences include defining clauses and which include non-defining clauses. Write *D* or *ND* in the box after each sentence.

a) the children who went to the ballet enjoyed themselves ☐

b) the children who went to the ballet enjoyed themselves ☐

c) the passengers who had eaten fish were ill ☐

d) the passengers who had eaten fish were ill ☐

e) I'm going to visit my brother who lives in New York ☐

f) I'm going to visit my brother who lives in New York ☐

g) the buildings which have been restored look lovely ☐

h) the buildings which have been restored look lovely ☐

WRITING

1 Punctuate the sentences in the preceding exercise, taking care to distinguish between defining relative clauses and non-defining relative clauses. Rewrite the punctuated sentences in your notebook.

2 Reduce the number of sentences in each paragraph of this text to one, by connecting them. For example:

One day Jane knocked on my door. (She lives in the same building as me.)
One day Jane, who lives in the same building as me, knocked on my door.

A
> A duchess plans to abseil from a 150-foot high hospital roof this weekend. She is doing this to raise funds for charity.

_____
_____
_____
_____

B
> The stunt by the duchess will mark the start of National Meningitis Awareness Week. The duchess is the sister of the Marquess of Bath.

_____
_____
_____

C
> "It is the scariest thing I can imagine. That is why I am doing it," said the 60-year-old duchess, wife of the 11th duke. His family seat is at Badminton Park.

_____
_____
_____

D
> The duchess is well-known for her unconventional behaviour. She recently swam in a piranha-infested river during a trip to Brazil.

_____
_____
_____

Girls + boys = mixed blessings

LEARNING GRAMMAR

Substitution

Substitute one word for the underlined parts of these sentences.

a) 'Do you think it will rain?' 'No, I don't think <u>it will rain</u>.'
I don't think so.

b) I can't decide whether to go to the cinema or <u>whether not to go to the cinema</u>.

_____

c) I used to like musicals but I haven't been to <u>a musical</u> for ages.

_____

d) She said she would write and she <u>wrote</u>.

_____

e) It was very hot and remained <u>very hot</u> for days.

_____

f) 'Have you got a dishwasher?' 'Yes, we've just bought <u>a dishwasher.</u>'

_____

g) Will you be going to the shops? If <u>you are going to the shops</u> could you get some bread?

_____

h) 'Would you like some cake?' 'I don't mind if I <u>have some cake.</u>'

_____

i) 'Is that my cigarette lighter?' 'No, it's <u>my cigarette lighter.</u>'

_____

j) 'Do you think it will rain?' 'I think <u>it won't rain.</u>'

_____

k) 'Do you promise to love, honour and obey her?' 'I <u>promise to love, honour and obey her.</u>'

_____

Ellipsis

1 Reduce these sentences by removing the suggested number of words.

a) She is working and at the same time she is bringing up her children. (-2)
She is working and at the same time bringing up her children.

b) We decided we would educate the girls exactly as we would educate the boys. (-1)

_____

c) She never finished her degree though now she wishes she had finished it. (-2)

_____

d) Margaret takes the girls on holiday and Mortimer takes the boys on holiday. (-3)

_____

e) Libby was good at maths, Tessa was good at languages, and Kate was good at games. (-6)

_____

f) Girls can be provided with the same educational opportunities, and must be provided with the same educational opportunities as boys are provided with educational opportunities. (-11)

_____

_____

_____

g) We believed in the right to educate our children and fought for the right to educate our children. (-6)

_____

_____

2 Using both substitution and ellipsis, reduce these texts to the minimum number of words. Rewrite them in your notebooks.

a) My primary school days had not been very happy and my secondary school days were not very happy either. For a start, my teachers didn't seem as concerned for me as they were concerned for the other children. Nor did I devote as much time to my studies as I should have devoted to them, perhaps. But more than that, I had the feeling that if I was developing as a human being I was developing as a human being not because of what they were trying to knock into me but in spite of what they were trying to knock into me. In short, I thought it was a waste of time. I wish now that I had said it was a waste of time then.

b) Because of these unhappy memories of my schooling (and because my wife had similar memories of her schooling) we decided that we would educate our own children at home. To educate our own children at home, naturally, required a radical reorganization of our daily routine. Had we not radically reorganized our daily routine, the children would have been left largely to their own devices. I arranged to work mainly afternoons and Sharon arranged to work mainly evenings. This way we had the mornings entirely free. A neighbour was keen to have her children join our children, giving us six in all. I dedicated myself to the younger boys and girls and Sharon dedicated herself to the older boys and girls.

VOCABULARY

Multi-part verb: verb + adverbial particle + preposition

1 List all the possible combinations of verbs (column A) and particles (column B) to make multi-part verbs.

A	B
a) come	1 up for
b) catch	2 up against
c) keep	3 away with
d) make	4 in for
e) put	5 up with
f) stand	6 up to
g) get	7 out of

2 Complete the following sentences with one of the multi-part verbs from Exercise 1.

a) She talked so fast, I couldn't *keep up with* what she was saying.

b) We _____ unexpected difficulties with the project and had to abandon it.

c) Josh is in trouble again: that boy finds it impossible to _____ mischief.

d) Forgive me for forgetting your birthday. I promise I'll _____ it.

e) The TV that was stolen was insured so I'm going to _____ £500.

f) Some people think they can _____ murder, but we intend to prove that crime does not pay.

g) How long do you think you can _____ that dog barking downstairs?

h) This government is not going to give in to pressure. We will _____ both the unions and the bosses.

i) She got off to a bad start but by the end of the race she had nearly _____ the winner.

j) The new housing scheme _____ review next month, so we will have a better idea as to how it has been working.

READING

Read these texts in which two Irish writers recall their childhood. Then answer the questions.

1 In what significant ways was Mary's experience different from Molly's?

_____

_____

2 a) What evidence is there that Molly had been educated at home?

_____

b) What evidence is there that Molly went to a secular school?

_____

c) What evidence is there that Mary went to a religious school?

_____

d) What evidence is there that Molly was good at English?

_____

e) What evidence is there that Mary lived at home?

_____

f) What evidence is there that Mary's father was uneducated?

_____

_____

3 Find words or expressions in the texts that are similar in meaning to the following:

Text A (Molly Keane):

a) way of training and caring for a child

_____

b) hideous _____

c) government _____

d) disobedient _____

Text B (Mary Lavin):

e) sociable _____

f) willingly _____

g) somebody good at both sports and study

_____

h) not feel guilty _____

i) kept in a confined space _____

A

Molly Keane

I went to school at a very late age - I must have been about fourteen. It was called the French School in Bray, Co. Wicklow, probably, I think, because it had been started by some old French lady a thousand years ago. A great-aunt of mine went there so it was pretty ancient.

It was a very odd place. Everybody, girls and teachers - except the English mistress - hated me. I suppose it was because I was a different kind of animal to them, having grown as old as I had in that very isolated way; whereas they had a different upbringing, and had seen much more of the neighbouring children as they grew up. It was a great shock to me, as I had always liked people. I had got on terribly well with all the people who worked at home but now I felt that life would be miserable for the rest of my life.

The school had a very strict régime. There were no 'naughty doings': even the smallest doing was supposed to be dreadfully naughty! You had to make a report each morning on how you had behaved the previous day. Speaking French was the big thing in that school, so the best report was 'I faithfully spoke French and I was punctual.' (You can imagine the awful French we spoke!) The next grade in the report was 'I faithfully <u>tried to speak</u> French and I was punctual'; and the worst grade of all was 'I didn't speak any French and I was late.' If you were honest enough to admit that, some ghastly punishment would follow.

Academically, I was hopeless. They gave up trying to teach me arithmetic, let alone mathematics! English was taught in a dreadfully bad and dull fashion; and as a result I don't think that I had any understanding of literature until I was at least twenty-five. But despite that I had a certain liking for it, and I loved Tennyson and Kipling especially.

B

Mary Lavin

Living in Dublin also meant that I could go to day school rather than boarding school. I went to Loreto Convent School in St Stephen's Green. I was so happy there. I loved it for a variety of reasons. I did well academically; being a gregarious type I loved meeting and mixing with other girls; also, I suppose there wasn't a great intellectual stimulus at home, so I responded readily to the challenge of school. At the same time I was not unduly forced to study at home.

I was a good all-rounder at school. My father had been a champion athlete in Co. Roscommon (or 'champeen', as they would say). The Loreto order had a big sports day for all their schools at which I picked up quite a lot of medals for running and jumping. My father always came to the sports - he loved to see me excel at sport.

He would come to the school at other times too. He wanted me to be well educated; he would say 'I want you to go to college, Mary, not like me.' But he would have no qualms either about walking into the school and taking me to Aintree for two or three days. The nuns were all terrified of him, because he would come in and call for Reverend Mother and say to her, 'I want to take Mary out for the day. It's a lovely fine day and I don't see why she should be cooped up here!'

(from *A Portrait of the Artist as a Young Girl* by John Quinn)

4 a) The school 'was pretty ancient' (Text A). Do you think:

    i) the school was really 1000 years old? ☐

    ii) the school was at least 100 years old? ☐

  b) 'There were no "naughty doings"' (Text A) means:

    i) everyone was well behaved? ☐

    ii) misbehaviour was not tolerated? ☐

  c) 'They gave up trying to teach me arithmetic, let alone mathematics!' (Text A) implies:

    i) mathematics was harder than arithmetic? ☐

    ii) mathematics was easier than arithmetic? ☐

e) He considered that the children were insufficiently disciplined.

_____

_____

f) You are too young. You can't go to school yet.

_____

_____

g) You need more qualifications for this job.

_____

_____

LANGUAGE PATTERNS

Enough

'If you were honest enough to admit that, some ghastly punishment would follow.'

    Note that *enough* always follows the adjective. It can be followed by *for* + noun phrase to indicate the person involved, or by *to* + the base form of the verb.

    Convert the following sentences into sentences using *enough*, trying to retain the original meaning.

a) The soup was too hot. I couldn't drink it.
    The soup wasn't cool enough to drink.

b) He was not sufficiently bright to go to university.

_____

_____

c) Brian was too short to be a policeman.

_____

_____

d) She lacked the necessary motivation to succeed.

_____

_____

WRITING

Cohesion

In the following text the writer has used an excessive number of cohesive ties. Remove these, leaving only those that are essential to the coherence of the text. Rewrite the text in your notebook.

As a matter of fact, education is an experience we all share. *In other words*, everyone at some time or other has been to school. *In short*, like work, like marriage, it is a universal human experience. *Consequently*, there are few of us who, when reminiscences of schooldays start to flow, can't contribute a tale of our own. *However*, they are not always happy stories. *On the contrary*, they are quite often harrowing. *Nevertheless*, they have a strong attraction. *For example*, was X – now a company director – beaten as a child? *On the other hand*, wasn't Y – permanently sedated these days – once top of her class? *In fact*, as Wordsworth wrote: 'The child is father of the man.' *Accordingly*, our school stories tell us not just where we've been, but who we are.

Looking ahead

▼

READING

Read this text and decide whether it is:

a) an advertisement
b) a news article
c) a manifesto
d) an encyclopaedia entry

GREENPEACE

BATTLES YET TO COME

These are the big issues which will preoccupy Greenpeace throughout the 1990s. Each, like Antarctica once seemed, appears almost too vast to complete. But unless these issues are tackled and won the final environmental challenge, of eliminating world poverty without destroying the course of natural evolution, cannot be effectively addressed.

Right now, Greenpeace is laying the foundations for future daring and imaginative campaigns on all of these issues.

1   Oil is the blood of the current world economy. But the age of fossil fuel dependence is drawing to a close. This must happen because the polluting emissions from burning fossil fuels are poisoning the atmosphere and threatening to wreck the world's climate patterns. This is the central challenge posed by global warming and all atmospheric pollution.

Greenpeace aims to steer the process of change towards what is known as a low energy future. Here energy efficiency becomes paramount and energy dependence is moved away from fossil and nuclear fuels towards renewable sources such as the sun.

2   Greenpeace aims to return the seas to their natural state. By this we mean that nothing poisonous will enter the sea from any human source and that the sea will be clear of pollution and safe for its wildlife to thrive in. This means ending all discharges of chemical waste and oil directly or indirectly into the sea. Greenpeace will also campaign to achieve and uphold an absolute ban on the dumping of toxic and nuclear wastes into the sea. Finally, the clean seas campaign will oppose the carriage of toxic or nuclear wastes across the sea.

3   The rainforests are the heart of the world, circulating warm, moisture laden air around the globe. They have to be protected and restored so that they can fulfil their ecological task of helping to maintain a climate and atmosphere which allows the natural evolution of life to continue.

The Greenpeace approach to rainforest campaigning will, as a priority, be led by Greenpeace offices which have been established within countries which host the rainforests. It is crucial to stop the destruction of the forests, often caused by the policies and patterns of consumption of developed countries. It is compounded by inequity and landlessness in the South.

Without some degree of equity in economic power between rich and poor nations, the environment of the latter will continue to be eroded and destroyed.

4   Life has evolved myriad species and made diversity its greatest source of strength.

But increasingly, human activity is destroying nature's biodiversity. Modern agricultural techniques are removing natural habitats and replacing the natural abundance of species with vast tracts of monocultured land which currently survives courtesy of chemical fertilizers and pesticides.

There is mounting evidence that chemically maintained monocultures are not sustainable. Soil erosion, alteration of water tables and resistance to pesticides are conspiring to undermine the so-called green revolution.

Now, by genetic manipulation, totally contrived species of plants and animals can be created and sustained in what may become very productive but largely artificial and highly simplified environments.

Greenpeace is fundamentally opposed to the loss of natural species and habitats which will follow from the widespread adoption of genetically manipulated species.

Greenpeace also opposes the owning and patenting of genetically engineered life forms. It is deeply concerned over the release of these life forms into the open environment, where the long term interaction between these and natural life forms cannot be predicted.

Issues surrounding genetic engineering may well become the central battleground of environmental campaigning in the last years of this century, and Greenpeace is already well versed in the subject.

1 For each of the four sections of the text, choose the most appropriate title from this list.

Global warming   Economic equity
Soil erosion   Nuclear wastes
Clean seas   Genetic engineering
Pollution   The South
Chemicals   Fossil fuels
Rainforests   Biodiversity
Energy

2 These sentences have been taken out of the text, one from each section. Can you replace them in the correct position?

a) How, and how quickly, can the world wean itself from fossil fuels?
b) This in turn means an end to all discharges into rivers, sewers and into the atmosphere.
c) One of our aims is to provide rainforest campaigns within these countries with the kind of resources and expertise developed and enjoyed in the rich countries where Greenpeace grew up.
d) This process in effect reverses natural evolution, which tends towards diversity.

3 Write *T* (for *True*) or *F* (for *False*) next to the statements below.

a) Greenpeace aims to replace fossil fuels with nuclear and solar energy. ☐
b) Greenpeace is campaigning against both the dumping and transporting of nuclear wastes in and across the seas. ☐
c) Greenpeace wants rich countries to put pressure on countries that have rainforests. ☐
d) Greenpeace supports the idea of a greater sharing of wealth between rich and poor countries. ☐
e) The 'green revolution' is proving to be a failure. ☐
f) The genetic engineering of new species is an example of biodiversity. ☐
g) Greenpeace argues that it may be risky to release new life forms into the environment. ☐

4 Find words or expressions in the text that are similar in meaning to the following:

Section 1:
a) destroy _____
b) become less dependent _____
c) of supreme importance _____

Section 2:
d) to prosper, flourish _____
e) prohibition _____

Section 3:
f) sphere _____
g) made more complicated _____

Section 4:
h) countless _____
i) large areas _____
j) subvert _____
k) legally protecting (an invention, discovery, etc.) _____
l) experienced _____

5 Underline the word which combines best with the following. (Use the text to check.)

a) There is (*enlarging/ rising/ mounting/ swelling*) evidence that ...
b) We are (*heartily/ basically/ widely/ fundamentally*) opposed to ...
c) Greenpeace is (*deeply/ fundamentally/ basically/ heartily*) concerned that ...
d) The Green movement is (*putting/ laying/ raising/ setting*) the foundations for ...
e) The 20th century is (*coming/ going/ drawing/ driving*) to a close ...
f) We intend to (*grasp/ grab/ tackle/ grapple*) these issues ...

TALKING EFFECTIVELY

Multi-syllable word stress

1 [15.1] Mark the stressed syllable in these words from the text on Greenpeace. Listen to the recording to check.

economy

environmental	equity
evolution	diversity
imaginative	agricultural
atmosphere	habitats
ecological	manipulation
priority	genetic
developed	engineering

2 [15.2] Mark the stress on these related words, and decide if the stressed syllable is the same as, or different from, the stressed syllable in Exercise 1. Listen to the recording to check.

economic (*different stress*)

environment	equitable
evolve	diverse
imagination	agriculture
atmospheric	habitable
ecology	manipulative
prioritise	geneticist
development	engineer

LEARNING GRAMMAR

Mixed conditionals

1 Look at these examples of conditional sentences taken from newspapers and magazines. Which are pure conditionals, and, if so, which type are they (i.e. types 1, 2 or 3), and which are mixed conditionals?

a) 'If they had panicked and run off, we would have been perfectly within our rights to shoot at them,' said a spokesman.
   pure conditional (type 3)

b) 'I would have been there tonight if I could have got a ticket,' he sighed.

c) Never mind the number of records they sell. If this was a fight it would've been declared null and void.

d) 'You're the best audience in the world,' says a delighted Kilby. 'And I wouldn't say that if it wasn't true.'

e) 'If you were to take all my furniture out of this flat it would just be how it was when I moved in.'

f) If you grow vegetables in conventional long rows, digging helps to control weeds.

g) Asked if he saw any potential conflict of interest in his appointment with Allied Lyons, he said: 'If I had, I wouldn't have done it.'

h) Comments like: 'If you don't pay up, the boys will put a brick through your window,' are among the scare tactics they use.

i) He always showed people the pictures he had made of them. If he could find the person, they would have seen their photograph.

j) Maybe if somebody would dye greengage jam to look like strawberry I might get to like it.

k) If he never returns, I would not be greatly surprised.

l) He said: 'If we are not going to win the World Cup then I do want England to win it.'

2   Underline the correct form of the verb to complete these sentences.

a) If the seas (*are not/will not be/would not be*) cleaned up, the world's fish supply is threatened.

b) If Greenpeace (*had not mounted/ did not mount/ does not mount*) a campaign, the Antarctic would now be a vast mining ground.

c) If genetic engineering (*is/will be*) unregulated, the delicate balance of nature (*will/would*) collapse.

d) If the rich countries (*will continue/ continued*) to import timber, the poor countries (*will continue/continued*) to supply it.

e) Unless the developed world (*accepts/accepted*) a drop in living standards, the future of the planet (*will be/ would be*) endangered.

f) If the rich countries (*weren't/hadn't been*) so greedy nowadays, the environment conference in 1992 (*would have been/would be*) a success.

g) If the price of petrol (*had not fallen/didn't fall*) in 1984, we (*would be/would have been*) driving electric cars now.

3   In these sentences, put the verb in brackets into the correct form.

a) If only I (*see*) _____ the red light!

b) I think it's time you (*have*) _____ a haircut.

c) I'd rather you (*play*) _____ outside, if you don't mind.

d) What if the dinosaurs (*survive*) _____!

e) Imagine if the sea (*rise*) _____ one metre: many of the world's largest cities would be flooded.

f) If I (*know*) _____ you were coming, I would have baked a cake.

g) Although they (*live*) _____ round the corner, we never visit them.

h) Even if they (*live*) _____ round the corner, we would never visit them.

i) Although, in those days, they (*live*) _____ round the corner, we would never visit them.

LANGUAGE PATTERNS

Suggestions and recommendations

Rewrite these sentences using the prompts so as to change the meaning as little as possible.

a) Greenpeace recommends closing nuclear power plants.
Greenpeace recommends that _____
_____

b) It is vital to clean up the oceans.
It is vital that _____
_____

c) It is essential that the rainforests be protected.
It is essential to _____
_____

d) Greenpeace proposes banning deep-sea mining.
Greenpeace proposes that _____
_____

e) They insist that the rich nations reduce their energy needs.
They insist on _____
_____

f) Greenpeace recommends reducing dependence on fossil fuels.
Greenpeace recommends that _____
_____

LISTENING

[📼 15.3] Listen to these people talking about the environment and complete the chart.

	Main worry	Personal contribution
1		
2		
3		
4		

WRITING

Topic and comment sentences

'Oil is the blood of the current world economy. But the age of fossil fuel dependence is drawing to a close.'

The first sentence in the extract on page 61 is the topic sentence and introduces the topic of the paragraph. The second sentence is a comment on the topic: it elaborates the topic sentence in some way.

In this text, adapted from *Greenpeace News*, the sentences have been re-arranged. Can you:

1 identify three topic sentences (*T*)?
2 identify two comment sentences (*C*) for each topic sentence?
3 put the text in order, dividing it into three paragraphs, with one topic sentence and two comment sentences in each paragraph? Rewrite the complete text in your notebook.

1 In just two years they reduced the rockcod population to just 2.5% of its original size. ☐

2 They support fish, seals and whales, among others. ☐

3 This century whale populations have been decimated. ☐

4 Antarctica's marine sources have long been plundered. ☐

5 Having depleted the rockcod, the Soviets turned on the mackerel icefish. ☐

6 The history of Antarctic fisheries exploitation is particularly worrying in the light of the krill industry. ☐

7 Even as early as the 1820s fur seals had been driven practically to extinction. ☐

8 The tiny shrimp-like krill are central to the Southern Ocean ecosystem. ☐

9 The Soviet Union has been a leading offender. ☐

Creators and creativity

▼

READING

Read this description of the way the Nobel Prize-winning author Patrick White wrote his novels. Then answer the questions.

1 Write *T* (for *True*) or *F* (for *False*) beside each statement.

a) White usually wrote three drafts of each novel. ☐

b) The first draft was the hardest to write. ☐

c) He only ever abandoned one novel. ☐

d) He wrote at speed, seldom getting stuck. ☐

e) The third draft was the most boring to write. ☐

f) He wrote the first draft with a fountain pen and the second draft with a biro. ☐

g) He typed only the third draft. ☐

h) He typed single-spaced in order to reduce the cost of postage. ☐

i) He expected the final draft to take longer than it in fact did. ☐

2 White uses a number of metaphors to describe the process of writing.

a) What metaphor does he use for the first draft?

_____

b) What metaphor does he use for the second draft?

_____

c) What metaphor does he use for his writing generally?

_____

(from *Patrick White: A Life* by David Marr)

HE HAD LONG SETTLED into a routine of writing only three drafts of each novel. The first draft was impressionistic, sketchy in places, and very private. Here he established the shape of the book, said roughly what he wanted to say, but pointed to ends yet to be reached. The first draft was a kind of childbirth, always the most painful and took the longest to write, 'dragged out, by tongs, a bloody mess'. In these months he found himself 'at loggerheads with everyone and everything'. He drank for 'the flashes' and used alcohol 'to cut the knots' in his writing. He only ever abandoned a novel towards the end of the first draft. If he finished this draft he finished the novel. During the first draft White most gave vent to the self-pity of writing. 'I hate it at present,' he told Dutton in the early stages of *Riders in the Chariot*. 'But on the whole I get very little pleasure out of writing; it is just something that comes over me like a recurring disease.'

He wrote with a fountain pen - later a biro - in a clear hand on bundles of lined foolscap paper. Most of the time he maintained a strong forward momentum, drafting not on the page but in his head. Though Lascaris reported White spending weeks wrestling with a single phrase, his output in these years suggests such tussles happened only at moments of exceptional difficulty.

Second drafts were a pleasure to write. 'Getting the first down on paper is sheer agony, and the third has something too irrevocable about it, not to say boring; but the second can make one feel quite godlike at times, with the right words slipping into one's head, and shapes forming out of chaos.' This was not childbirth but engineering: White always spoke of second drafts as oxywelding.

The final draft was typed on his portable Olivetti. White typed with two fingers, single-spaced, keeping only very narrow margins on flimsy, almost transparent paper. These crowded pages drove his publishers to distraction, but White was worried about the price of stamps.

As usual he worked far more quickly on the final draft than he first expected; and as usual he suffered a terrible crisis of confidence as he neared the end. Would anyone be interested? Was he speaking a private language? Should he, even at this late stage, throw it away?

3   Find words or expressions in the text that mean:

a) lacking detail or finish

_____

b) on bad terms

_____

c) freely expressed (an opinion, etc.)

_____

d) repeating

_____

e) struggling

_____

f) struggles

_____

g) final

_____

h) joining metal using burning gas

_____

i) delicate

_____

j) made (them) frustrated and angry

_____

LANGUAGE PATTERNS

to + base form of verb after complements

Second drafts were a pleasure to write.

Noun and adjective complements can be followed by *to* + base form of the verb in order to make a comment. Note that intransitive verbs must be followed by a preposition. For example:

He was easy to please.
They were a pleasure to talk to.

Rewrite the following sentences, beginning with the prompts provided and using the above pattern.

a) It was easy teaching the junior class.
    The junior class was easy to teach.

b) Eating fresh fruit is good.
    Fresh fruit _____

c) It's difficult, working with you.
    You _____

d) It's not easy learning phrasal verbs.
    Phrasal verbs _____

e) Remembering the holiday was painful.
    The holiday_____

f) Sharing a flat with her was a pleasure.
    She _____

g) It was difficult following her lecture.
    Her lecture _____

h) Talking to him is pleasant.
    He _____

i) It's a headache, owning a car.
    A car _____

LEARNING GRAMMAR

Hopes and wishes

1   Match the two halves of each of these sentences.

A	B
a) I wish she could stay	1 but it was simply not possible.
b) I hope she can stay	2 but she insists on leaving.
c) I wish she had stayed	3 but she says she can't.
d) I wish she would stay	4 and I've prepared her room, just in case.
e) I hope she stayed	5 and I think she probably did.

2   Choose the correct form of the verb:

a) I really wish you (*phone*) _____ me. I waited for over an hour.

b) I wish you (*answer*) _____ those letters. They have been sitting on your desk for a week.

c) I hope you (*visit*) _____ the museum when you were in Cairo.

d) I hope you (*be*) _____ warm enough in London next week.

e) I wish Rosie (*like*) _____ fish: it's impossible to know what to cook for her.

f) I hope they (*like*) _____ fish, because there's nothing else to give them.

g) If only you (*have*) _____ a driver's licence: this job is perfect for you, otherwise.

h) I wish I (*drive*) _____. I'd love to own a car.

3   Convert these statements into wishes.

a) He never phoned!
I wish he had phoned.

b) I lost my address book!

_____

c) He won't keep quiet!

_____

d) I haven't got a video!

_____

e) Will it rain? I hope so!

_____

f) I can't type!

_____

g) I failed the entrance test!

_____

h) You lied to me!

_____

i) I'm so fat!

_____

VOCABULARY

Collocations

Underline the correct word to complete these sentences.

a) They have been (*saying/telling*) tales about me that are simply not true.

b) Now you must (*say/tell*) the truth: did you chop down the tree?

c) Yes, it was me. I cannot (*say/tell*) a lie.

d) He told us a tall (*story/tale*) about why he had been delayed. It was totally unbelievable.

e) Well, to cut a long (*story/tale*) short, I got there just as the train was leaving.

f) She read the children a fairy (*tale/story*) about a princess and a frog.

g) Give him a drink and he will tell you his whole life (*story/tale*).

h) Show me your palm and I will (*say/tell*) your fortune.

WRITING

Punctuation

Punctuate this text. Rewrite it in your notebook.

patrick whites great grandfather went from england to australia in 1826 and the family has remained there mr white was born in england in 1912 when his parents were in europe for two years at six months he was taken back to australia where his father owned a sheep station when he was thirteen he was sent to school in england to cheltenham where in his words it was understood the climate would be temperate and a colonial acceptable neither proved true and after four rather miserable years there he went to kings college cambridge where he specialized in languages after leaving the university he settled in london determined to become a writer his novel happy valley was published in 1939 the living and the dead in 1941 then during the war he was an raf intelligence officer in the middle east and greece

A world of difference

READING

Read this poem by Philip Larkin, and answer the questions.

The Winter Palace

1   Most people know more as they get older:
    I give all that the cold shoulder.

2   I spent my second quarter-century
    Losing what I had learnt at university

3   And refusing to take in what had happened since.
    Now I know none of the names in the public prints,

4   And am starting to give offence by forgetting faces
    And swearing I've never been in certain places.

5   It will be worth it, if in the end I manage
    To blank out whatever it is that is doing the damage.

6   Then there will be nothing I know.
    My mind will fold into itself, like fields, like snow.

(from *The Winter Palace* by Philip Larkin)

1 Tick which statement you think best summarises the poem.

a) The poet grows old, and is worried about losing his memory. ☐

b) The poet grows old, and is pleased to be forgetting everything he once knew. ☐

c) The poet grows old, and regrets his past life. ☐

2 Match these paraphrases with the stanzas (1 - 6) of the poem.

a) I look forward to my memory going completely. ☐

b) Everything they once taught me I have steadily forgotten. ☐

c) One day my mind will be completely empty. ☐

d) I'm not interested in accumulating knowledge, like most ageing people do. ☐

e) I've not kept up-to-date with news and current affairs. ☐

f) People are getting annoyed with my bad memory. ☐

3 Find words or expressions that mean:

a) twenty-five years _____

b) to erase _____

c) I ignore it _____

d) claiming _____

e) newspapers, magazines, etc. _____

f) to absorb _____

4 Which do you think is the best explanation of the title of the poem? Tick the appropriate box.

a) He imagines his mind will one day be empty and cold, like a palace in winter. ☐

b) Probably he wrote it while or after visiting a winter palace. ☐

c) The poem is about an imaginary king, exiled and alone in his winter palace. ☐

d) Old age is cold and bleak, like winter. ☐

5 The final image of the poem is one of:

a) emptiness and/or whiteness. ☐

b) smallness and/or flatness. ☐

c) coldness. ☐

LEARNING GRAMMAR

Comparisons

1 Correct these examples of student mistakes.

a) It all happen when I was very younger.

_____

b) I was the person happier in all the world.

_____
_____

c) Pierre is same intelligent as me.

_____

d) People doesn't work as hardly as they thinks.

_____
_____

e) He looks more younger than he really is.

_____

f) There are more worse things that could happen to you if you drink.

_____
_____

g) She is worse student than me and she is the fast runner of girls in the class.

_____
_____

h) I'm too much tired on holiday that in my work.

_____
_____

2 Use the prompts to make statements about processes using *get* + the repeated comparative.

a) (*The nights/cold*)
   The nights are getting colder and colder.

b) (*My memory/bad*) _____
   _____

c) (*Our English class/good*) _____
   _____

d) (*These exercises/difficult*) _____
   _____

e) (*Grammar/interesting*) _____
   _____

f) (*The boys/good-looking*) _____
   _____

g) (*Our employees/well-paid*) _____
   _____

3 Complete these sentences, using *the* + comparative + *the* + comparative construction.

a) 'What time shall we come?' 'Come early. In fact _the earlier the better_.'

b) 'How short do you want your hair?' 'Very short. In fact _____

c) 'Which strawberries shall I buy?' 'The cheap ones. In fact _____

d) 'How far away shall I bury the rubbish?' 'The _____

e) 'I'm going away for a long time!' 'Good. The _____

f) 'How many people shall we invite?' 'As many as possible. The _____

g) 'I'll take you out to eat – somewhere expensive.' 'Oh good. The _____
   _____

4 Complete this text by choosing words from the box below.

in	better	harmful	as (x2)	more	still
such	kinder	getting	likely	performed	

• •

To judge by *Which?* members' responses in our survey, most people are happy with the detergent they use. But some brands are better at ¹ _____ stains out, some may be ² _____ to your skin, and some are less ³ _____ to harm the environment. Here we give a summary of our findings.
● Some detergents are ⁴ _____ than others at removing tough stains ⁵ _____ as cocoa, blood and wine. The detergents that ⁶ _____ best in our stain removal test are all powders.
● ⁷ _____ our tests most liquids didn't work ⁸ _____ well at removing stains ⁹ _____ most powders. But you may ¹⁰ _____ want to buy a liquid because it could be ¹¹ _____ to your skin, and liquids can be ¹² _____ convenient to use.

5 Complete these English sayings, using the comparative form of the adjectives in the box below.

> short   careless   welcome   small
> far   bad   old   near   high

a) The better workman, the _____ husband.

b) The worse the passage, the _____ the port.

c) The _____ the peas, the more to the pot.

d) The _____ the bone, the sweeter the flesh.

e) The nearer the church, the _____ from God.

f) The more light a torch gives, the _____ it lasts.

g) The _____, the more modish.

h) The _____ the hill, the lower the grass.

Now, match the proverb with its interpretation:

1 People with good fortune are not the most generous. ☐

2 To dress untidily is very fashionable. ☐

3 The most pious are not always the most holy. ☐

4 Never mind if the journey is bad – you'll feel even happier when you get home. ☐

5 Good things don't have to be big. ☐

6 Beauty is not on the surface. ☐

7 If your husband is a good worker, he'll never be at home. ☐

8 Good things don't last long. ☐

LANGUAGE PATTERNS

Like and *as*

Complete this text, using *like* or *as*.

_____ I get older, I get more and more _____ my father. Although I'm not _____ bald _____ he was in his old age, I'm starting to lose my hair, and, _____ he always used to say, 'The fewer, the wiser.' It often seems to me _____ if children start to look more _____ their parents the more they start to understand them. My father and I used to fight _____ cat and dog, especially in the days when I was working _____ a singer in a band and looked _____ if I didn't have a penny to my name. In those days, few people realised we were related. Nowadays, _____ I said before, we grow more and more _____ each other, both in outlook and appearance.

VOCABULARY

Idioms of comparison

There are many idioms of comparison in English; *as large as life* and *as busy as a bee* are just two.

Complete the following common idioms, using the words in the box.

> a hatter   a bat   a judge   clockwork   jet
> a cucumber   a feather   gold   the hills
> a daisy

a) as black as *jet*

b) as light as _____

c) as old as _____

d) as regular as _____

e) as good as _____

f) as sober as _____

g) as mad as _____

h) as fresh as _____

i) as cool as _____

j) as blind as _____

LISTENING

[🖭 17.1] Listen to these four people talking about growing old, and fill in the chart.

	What they fear	What they look forward to	How they hope to stay young
1			
2			
3			
4			

WRITING

Read this text, and imagine you have been asked to write a shortened version of it for a local newspaper. In your notebook, summarise the main points in not more than 100 words, rearranging the text to make the newsworthy information more prominent, if necessary. Remember that you are writing for a non-specialist readership.

Who wants to live forever?

GROWING old does not increase your immediate risk of dying - at least, if you are a fruit fly. The chances of a Mediterranean fruit fly (*Ceratitis capitata*) dying out on a particular day reaches a peak and then declines, according to James Carey of the University of California and Davis and James Vaupel of Duke University, North Carolina. Their results contradict the notion that the death rate rises with age in all species.

The research will fan the flames of a long-running debate over whether or not there is a genetically defined limit to an individual's lifespan. If there is not and the fruit fly results extend to humans, then medical advances might eventually allow the elderly to live indefinitely.

In the early 19th century, the British statistician Benjamin Gompertz formulated a law stating that mortality rates increase with age. For an adult human the immediate chance of death seems to double every eight years. The Gompertz law was believed to hold for all species and to put an age limit on each species.

To test this theory, Carey and Vaupel studied more than a million fruit flies. They found that the death rate reached a maximum of about 15 per cent when the flies were between 40 and 60 days old, and then fell. Flies that survived to 100 days had only a 4 to 6 per cent chance of dying on a given day. In other words, the chances of dying seem not to increase sharply in advanced age, as predicted by the Gompertz law; rather, they seem to level off.

If the Gompertz law does not hold for human beings either, then there may be no genetically defined limit on a person's lifespan.

(from *New Scientist*)

A current affairs documentary

VOCABULARY

The Media

Match the job with the definition.

a) reporter
b) producer
c) journalist
d) newsreader
e) anchorman
f) editor
g) publisher
h) cameraman
i) cinematographer

1 the person who organises the parts of a film or programme into a unified sequence; also, the person responsible for the content of a newspaper, or a part of one.
2 the person or firm that produces and distributes a book, newspaper, magazine, etc.
3 a person who gathers and reports news for a newspaper or a news broadcast
4 a person who makes films
5 a person who operates a camera
6 a person who co-ordinates the different reports, interviews, etc. in a news broadcast
7 a person employed to write for a newspaper
8 a person who reads aloud news reports on radio or TV
9 a person responsible for the overall production of a film or programme; in films, the person responsible for controlling the money

READING

Read this extract from a novel and answer the questions overleaf.

Sybille seemed taller in the control room, even when she was sitting down. She wore a brown pinstripe suit with a white blouse that tied in a small bow at her throat; Nick thought she looked formidable. Often she stood as she talked on the telephone or bent over to make notes
5 at the long narrow desk with telephones, notepads, and clusters of buttons that connected her to everyone in the studio and other parts of the building. When she sat in her upholstered executive chair on the upper level of the large room, she had the air, Nick reflected, of a ruler surveying her kingdom. Below her sat the director and assistant director and, beside them,
10 in his own space, the technical director with his enormous panel of lights and buttons that looked as if it came from the cockpit of a jumbo jet. Looking past them, Sybille could scan the banks of TV screens filling the wall of the control room, some of them showing what each camera in the studio was focusing on at the moment, others showing reporters at remote
15 locations, still others showing taped segments, and titles and graphics.

Nick and Chad sat on a bench behind Sybille, their eyes moving back and forth from her and her assistant producer at the long desk to the screens on the wall. When Sybille picked up one of her three telephones, pushed a button on the panel before her, and said, "Warren, pick up your telephone,"
20 they saw the anchorman in the studio, who had heard her on his earplug, reach out of camera range and bring a bright-red telephone to his ear. "We've got a new expert on the Exeter nuclear plant," she said, "so we're moving the story back: we'll run it as soon as he gets here. I'm writing a new lead; I'll let you know when he's here."
25 Nick saw the man on the screen talk protestingly into the telephone. Sybille was writing on the program schedule before her, the phone wedged between her shoulder and chin, but as the man talked her fingers stilled. "It *was* the top story; it isn't anymore. Your lead was fine, but we need a new one for this guy, and I've written it. It's done." He spoke again; Nick heard
30 his raised voice through the telephone, cut off by Sybille's icy words. "Warren, I'll say this once, so you'd better get it. No one else has this guy; he's always refused to go public. I found him, I'm using him, and you'll talk to him when I tell you to. If you can't handle that, you can come to my office after the show and tell me why not. And fix your handkerchief; it's
35 crooked." She slammed down the telephone and went back to revising the hour-long program schedule. On one of the television screens in the wall before her, Warren's red face seemed to swell, then shrivel. He rotated his head as if his collar were too tight. Slowly, he raised a hand and straightened the handkerchief in his pocket.
40 Below Sybille, the director shook his head. "A killer," he murmured to the assistant director, and no one seemed to care that, of course, Sybille heard it.

Nick held Chad on his lap and remembered the tearful, hesitant girl who had told him about being expelled from college and fired from her job. And
45 now, in this control room, she was a ruler surveying her kingdom. A killer.

(from *A Ruling Passion* by Judith Michael)

Tick the correct answers.

1   What is happening?

a) They are shooting a film. ☐
b) They are preparing a current affairs
   programme. ☐
c) They are preparing a news broadcast. ☐
d) They are rehearsing a play. ☐
e) They are editing a newspaper. ☐

2   Who is Sybille?

a) the producer ☐   b) the director ☐
c) the newsreader ☐   d) a reporter ☐

3   Who is 'the man on the screen'? (line 25)

a) the nuclear expert ☐   b) Warren ☐
c) Nick ☐   d) the director ☐

4   Who is Warren?

a) the assistant director ☐
b) the assistant producer ☐
c) the anchorman ☐
d) the director ☐

5   Who is Chad?

a) a reporter ☐   b) a boyfriend ☐
c) a child ☐   d) the assistant producer ☐

6   Who is 'this guy'? (line 29)

a) a killer ☐   b) an expert on the nuclear
                      plant at Exeter ☐
c) Nick ☐   d) Warren ☐

7   Who is 'a killer'? (line 40)

a) Sybille ☐   b) Warren ☐
c) the nuclear expert ☐   d) the director ☐

8   Who is 'the tearful hesitant girl'? (line 43)

a) Warren ☐   b) Sybille ☐
c) the director ☐ d) none of these ☐

9   'Nick saw the man on the screen talk
protestingly into the telephone.' What did the
man on the screen probably say?

a) 'But this is the top story and I have written a
   good lead.' ☐

b) 'I can't talk to him now - the programme has
   already started.' ☐
c) 'But this wasn't the top story - and who's going
   to write the lead?' ☐
d) 'My lead was fine so why do we need a new
   one?' ☐

10   Circle the words or expressions which
could replace the following in the text.

a) formidable (line 3)
   i) wonderful   ii) terrific   iii) powerful
b) air (line 8)
   i) appearance   ii) atmosphere   iii) style
c) surveying (line 8)
   i) measuring   ii) viewing   iii) ruling
d) lead (line 24)
   i) introduction   ii) heading   iii) title
e) stilled (line 27)
   i) stayed   ii) tensed   iii) stopped moving
f) handle (line 33)
   i) hold   ii) accept   iii) understand
g) shrivel (line 37)
   i) contract   ii) dry up   iii) wrinkle
h) murmured (line 40)
   i) mumbled   ii) stuttered   iii) whispered

LEARNING GRAMMAR

Focussing on information: auxiliary verbs

1   Make the following statements more
emphatic, either by stressing the auxiliary (e.g.
must) or by using emphatic *do*.

a) I've never had squid but I have had octopus.

_____

_____

b) I never saw *The Birds* but I saw *Psycho*.

_____

_____

c) I don't like Handel but I like Purcell.

_____

_____

d) He can't play very well, but he can sing
   beautifully.

_____

_____

_____

e) 'You haven't cleaned your teeth.' 'I have cleaned them.'

_____

_____

f) 'You didn't do your homework.' 'I did it.'

_____

_____

2   Join each of these pairs of sentences by marking the contrast and adding emphasis where appropriate.

a) I don't take sugar. I take milk, however.
   I don't take milk but I do take sugar.

b) I don't like some things about New York. I like my apartment, though.

_____

_____

c) I don't worship success. I believe in hard work, though.

_____

_____

d) We didn't change the world. We changed people's attitudes, however.

_____

_____

e) She doesn't look like her mother. She has some of her mother's character, though.

_____

_____

f) We didn't go to Macy's. We went to Bloomingdales, though.

_____

_____

g) He doesn't do any cleaning. He does the dishes, however.

_____

_____

Focussing on information: cleft sentences

1   In the following sentences focus on the different elements of information (subject, verb, object, etc.) according to the prompts.

a) Wendy made cocoa for Mr Amis.
   (*subject*) _It was Wendy who made cocoa for Mr Amis._

(*verb*) _What Wendy did was make cocoa for Mr Amis._

(*object*) _It was cocoa that Wendy made for Mr Amis._

(*adverbial*) _It was Mr Amis who Wendy made cocoa for._

b) Columbus discovered America in 1492. (*adverbial*)

_____

_____

c) John Wilkes Booth shot Lincoln. (*subject*)

_____

_____

d) Wren designed St Paul's Cathedral. (*object*)

_____

_____

e) Joyce wrote *Ulysses* in Zurich. (*adverbial*)

_____

_____

f) Visconti made a film of *Death in Venice*. (*subject*)

_____

_____

g) Isabel Burton burnt her husband's diaries. (*verb*)

_____

_____

h) Gauguin died in Tahiti. (*adverbial*)

_____

_____

i) Verdi wrote an opera about Othello. (*verb*)

_____

_____

j) Kafka died in 1924. (*adverbial*)

_____

_____

2   In order to focus on what was done in these sentences use cleft sentences. Use the past tense if required.

a) She couldn't turn left. So she turned right.
   So what she did was turn right.

b) He can't drive. So he walks everywhere.

_____

_____

c) I can't read small print. So I use a magnifying glass.

_____

_____

d) I used to have trouble learning vocabulary. So I kept a notebook of new words.

_____

_____

e) She couldn't get to sleep. So she made herself a hot drink.

_____

_____

f) His job is very stressful. So he does yoga.

_____

g) She couldn't find a novel she liked. So she wrote one herself.

_____

_____

h) It was after midnight. So he took a taxi.

_____

3   Correct the misunderstandings in this dialogue by using cleft sentence constructions and by using the prompts provided.

A: So you went to Italy next, did you?

B: (*No, what/Spain*) _No, what we did was go to Spain._

A: And you stayed with Margaret?

B: (*No, it/Helen*) _____

_____

A: And you bought a car, didn't you?

B: (*No, what/hire*) _____

_____

A: And Gary had an accident, I gather?

B: (*No, it/me*) _____

_____

A: And you went skiing in the mountains?

B: (*No, what/go walking*) _____

_____

A: And you came back last Tuesday, right?

B: (*No, it/Monday*) _____

_____

TALKING EFFECTIVELY

Question tags

[🔲 18.1] Listen to the recording and decide, in each case, whether the question tag is rising (*R*) or falling (*F*).

a) We've met before, haven't we? ☐

b) We've met before, haven't we? ☐

c) They said it was going to rain, didn't they? ☐

d) They said it was going to rain, didn't they? ☐

e) You will write, won't you? ☐

f) You haven't lost it, have you? ☐

g) It's a lovely day, isn't it? ☐

h) You take milk in coffee, don't you? ☐

i) It was a great match, wasn't it? ☐

j) This is the right street, isn't it? ☐

Sentence stress

[🔲 18.2] Predict the stressed word in the numbered sentences, and then listen to the cassette to check.

A: Isn't it Tom and Vivian's anniversary next month?

B: No. (1) It was in June when they got married.

A: Are you sure it wasn't May?

B: (2) It was in May when we got married.

A: But I'm sure Tom and Vivian did something in May.

B: (3) It was May that they got engaged.

A: That's right. Tom proposed to Vivian.

B: No, (4) it was Vivian who proposed to Tom.

A: No, (5) it was Evelyn who proposed to Tom.

B: You're right. (6) It was Tom who proposed to Vivian.

LANGUAGE PATTERNS

No matter, whatever, however, etc.

Rewrite the following sentences so that they
express greater emphasis, using the prompts
provided.

a) Every time he phones, I'm in the bath.
    Whenever _____
    _____

b) I couldn't do anything to open the window.
    No matter _____
    _____

c) Even though I practise a lot, my Spanish never
    seems to improve.
    However _____
    _____

d) Every time I go shopping, I buy something I
    don't need.
    Whenever _____
    _____

e) I try and try, but I can never a finish a novel by
    Henry James.
    However _____
    _____

f) If we go left or if we go right, there's no exit.
    Whichever _____
    _____

WRITING

Information structure

Read this text and rewrite it in your notebook so
that the information in each sentence is organised
more coherently and more elegantly.

Djuha's Meat Disappears

In the market three kilos of lamb's meat was
bought by Djuha one day and what he did
was take it home to his wife. Out again he
went, after explaining to her how he would
like to have it prepared for his dinner.

The meat was seasoned and cooked
carefully by Djuha's wife. But she sent for
her brother and until nothing was left the
two of them feasted on it, it smelled so
delicious.

It was when Djuha came home and asked
for his dinner that his wife wailed, "For
dinner I have nothing to give you because it
was the cat that ran in and ate up the meat
while in the kitchen I was busy."

The scale tipped at exactly three kilos
when Djuha grabbed the cat and set it on it.
Djuha said, "Then where is the cat if this is
the meat? And, then tell me, where is the
meat, if this is the cat ...?"

Tapescripts

Unit 1

RECORDING 1 Memory

PSYCHOLOGIST: Basically there are different kinds of memory so when we talk about 'losing your memory' – well, I mean from a medical point of view, that's rather unsatisfactory.

INTERVIEWER: You mean it's not precise enough?

P: Exactly.

I: So what different types of memory are there?

P: Well, to start with there's what's called 'episodic memory' – that is, when you remember particular past events like, for example, your first day at school, or the circumstances of meeting your loved one, and so on. Or, of course, less dramatic things, like doing the shopping yesterday morning. Then, there's what's called 'factual memory', which, obviously enough, is the capacity to remember facts, such as the date King Charles was executed, or your best friend's birthday, or the capital of Mongolia and so on.

I: The sort of things you have to learn at school.

P: Yes, that's right. A lot of education – well traditionally anyway – encouraged the memorising of large numbers of facts. As well as these two types of memory, there's 'semantic memory', which is how we remember the meanings of words or of road signs and so on.

I: Not the sort of memory you lose?

P: That's right. Even amnesiacs – people who lose their memory, so to speak – usually retain the ability to speak their own language.

I: Are there any other types of memory?

P: Well, there's 'skill memory', for example, which is the ability to perform a function accurately, such as driving a car or even something as basic as getting dressed, or shaving or changing a lightbulb. And what is sometimes called 'sensory memory', that is the ability to recall sensations, such as the taste of, say, a mango, or the sound of the sea, or a particular painting, or a person's face. It's perhaps difficult to distinguish this from episodic memory. And even semantic memory can overlap with both sensory and episodic memory, as often is the case when you learn a new word in a foreign language – you often remember the circumstances in which you learnt it, and the sensations that accompanied that learning, especially if they're strong sensations such as excitement or anger or embarrassment, et cetera.

I: So, when we get old and start to 'lose our memory', what memory are we losing?

P: In the normal ageing process – I mean apart from the onset of certain diseases such as Alzheimer's disease, or nervous disorders, brain damage and so on – the memory that tends to become less efficient is episodic memory, particularly of rather trivial things, such as 'Where did I put my glasses?' Most adults are familiar with the sensation of not being able to remember anything about a film they saw or a book they read, even quite recently. Interestingly, the ability to remember facts doesn't diminish greatly with age and, as we said, semantic memory is not impaired at all. Nor is skill or sensory memory.

I: This suggests that even elderly people should be able to learn new skills and new languages without too much trouble?

P: Well, in a way, yes, although we should be careful of confusing the ability to remember previously learned skills and meanings with the capacity to learn new ones. Other factors, like motivation, attention and so on are important here. But no, learning can and does continue into advanced old age.

Unit 3

RECORDING 2 Holiday memories

1: When I was small, in Hampshire, we went on HMS Duneera which was a troop ship they used to er... schoolboys went on and we went to Venice, Greece and Turkey and erm some of the things I remember most of all was, er, standing in Greece and picking an orange off a tree and I'd never eaten an orange from the wild like that and when we pulled it off the tree and then peeled it, it was so incredibly bitter that it dried... my entire mouth dried right up, you know, and I needed a bucket of water afterwards. Erm, and Istanbul, I remember, that was incredible. We went to the Blue Mosque and er I remember the bazaars as well. We went into the Muslim Bazaar and I can remember drinking... they like to drink tea there and they drink it in glasses and erm then put two huge lumps of sugar in the glass. It's like a sherry glass and it's so sweet. Course I enjoyed that being as I was only fifteen years old but that's what I remember most about Istanbul. And it rained all the time.

2: Well, my dad was a teacher so we used to get like three months off in the summer and we always went up to an old place that he bought up in Maine. We had seventeen acres of land and beaches and we'd go sailing and swimming and, well, we usually spent the first month clearing up after the winter storms. And of course what we ate was lobster 'cause we could catch them right off the end of the dock so it was lobster and steamed clams, corn on the cob. Oh it was great!

3: I remember an absolutely magic day when I was little when my mom took my brother and my sister and I to Catalina Island off the coast of California. And we got on a big, big ferry – it's big because you're only seven years old – and took the twenty six mile trip to the island. And we had a picnic on the ferry that my mom made – typical American picnic: fried chicken, potato salad, water melon for dessert and she'd made some chocolate-chip cookies that were so awful that we fed them all to the seagulls that were following the ferry over there. And then when we got to the island we spent the whole day on the beach which was just wonderful. She bought me a, erm, a shovel and a bucket, you know, to play in the sand, by one of the little shops lining the beach. And we had hamburgers and hot dogs , french fries and then candy apples and cotton candy and popcorn. And I can remember taking the ferry home that night and wanting desperately to stay awake but I was so full of food that I slept the entire trip back.

4: Well, when I was child we lived in Canada, where it's very cold and nasty in the wintertime – endless snow. So most years we would try to go to Florida round about March or April. And it would take three days to drive down. You'd stop off at places en route. And gradually the weather would get warmer and warmer and the great thing was when you crossed the State line into Florida and you'd suddenly seem to see oranges growing on the trees and the sun was out and it was warm. And you'd drive to the beaches and it was just beautiful after all that snow. And, I remember, there were no theme parks then but the beaches seemed to be enough. There were beautiful sandy beaches and saltwater taffee, Florida orange juice and wonderful seafood. I think Red Snapper was our favourite fish, maybe because we liked the name. But oh it was just wonderful after all that cold and misery. And we used to cry when we left Florida and had to go back to the cold and snow.

Unit 5

RECORDING 1 Personal experiences

1: We had an amazing coincidence happen once. I was with all my friends in Las Vegas, Nevada, staying at one of the big casino hotels. And we'd all gotten dressed up for dinner and we were really excited and we came down in the elevator and they were playing Chubby Checker's song Let's twist again on the elevator. So, you know, we were in kind of a buoyant mood so we started singing to the song and dancing, doing the twist in the elevator, you know, all of us in the small, packed elevator.

Got down to the ground floor and the elevator opened and Chubby Checker was standing in front of all of us. We all kind of went quiet for a second with amazement. Then just started screaming with excitement and I must say, he was very gracious about these fifteen people coming piling off the elevator screaming at him.

2: I was working in a summerstock theatre and we were doing a show called *Charley's Aunt*. And we were having a little bit of a problem with the electricity – it was a very hot summer and if it got too hot in the theatre everything would just go dark. So there was this line that this actor had and it was: 'At first I was terribly afraid, especially of the man with the dark moustache.' So, he was doing the show, and he said, 'At first I was afraid...' and then all the lights went out and he said, 'especially of the dark!'

3: I had to call somebody up on the telephone and this was somebody that I didn't normally speak to on the telephone. I had no real reason to be calling her up normally and I couldn't find her phone number anywhere at all. And eventually I picked up the telephone to speak to directory enquiries to find out her number and there was a woman speaking on the other end. And it took me about fifteen or twenty seconds to manage to find out that this was the person that I had been trying to telephone. She had been trying to telephone me at the same time and there was absolutely no reason why she ought to be phoning me normally. She had by chance needed to call me and I picked up the phone without it ringing and she was on the other end.

Unit 7

RECORDING 1 Shopping in Hong Kong

INTERVIEWER: ...and now, as promised, here to talk to us about shopping in Hong Kong is Ta Lung of the Hong Kong Tourist Association. Ta Lung, a lot of listeners will be interested in typical Chinese items, such as jade and lacquerware. Is Hong Kong a good place to buy these?

TA LUNG: Yes, very much so. Excellent lacquerware can be found in Hong Kong for very reasonable prices along with traditional dolls, bamboo items and so on, and the best place for these is the China Product stores. You can also find things like acupuncture kits and Tiger Balm ointment there as well.

I: And where are these stores?

TL: You can find China Product stores on both sides of the harbour – the branch near the Star Ferry concourse on Kowloon is probably one of the easiest to find.

I: And jade?

TL: Well, actually, there's a special Jade Market, which is open every day on Kowloon under the Kansu Street flyover. This is probably the best place for jade.

I: Any advice for listeners about jade?

TL: Well, they say that the best way to test real jade is to sprinkle water on it. If it's genuine, little drops of water will form on the surface. Alternatively, you can try scratching it – plastic will mark but jade will not.

I: Sounds a bit risky, if you ask me. Talking of fake items, Hong Kong is a good place to find copies of designer clothing, I'm told.

TL: Well, I shouldn't say too much about that. But if visitors are interested in imitation Hermes scarves, Stanley Market is probably the place to go. That's on Hong Kong island itself, in what used to be a fishing village on the south coast. That's where you'll find fake Samsonite suitcases, as well as copy designer watches, I'm told. You can also get some good quality Chinese items there, too, like Chinese cashmere sweaters, for example.

I: And handbags?

TL: Well, there's an area which specialises in leather goods, and that's called the laneways; those are the narrow streets in the Central district of Hong Kong island, near the Lane Crawford department store. Here you'll find mountains of fake Chanel handbags. It's also a good place for cheap silks. I should mention the Western Market, too, which is in the same area: it's a covered market that has recently been restored, and it's a good place to buy cloth if you're having some clothes made locally. There are also traditional Chinese products for sale here, too, like hand-crafted stationery items and woodblock prints.

I: Now, I remember being fascinated by the night markets...

TL: Yes, these are wonderful places to visit. They open from about six in the evening: there's lots to eat and to look at, and the whole place is very noisy. They sell a lot of discount cassettes there, for example. The best night market is probably the Temple Street Market, off Jordan Road in Kowloon.

I: Any other tips?

TL: Well, we at the Hong Kong Tourist Association have produced a booklet with details about different factory outlets, where you can get very good value, for example with slightly flawed or damaged items, such as jewellery and clothing, but these 'seconds' are of very good quality. Most of these factory outlets are on the Hung Hom industrial estate in Kowloon.

Unit 9

RECORDING 1 Nicholas Jose

INTERVIEWER: Nicholas Jose, your novel 'Avenue of Eternal Peace' is about to be released as a television mini-series. Tell us a bit about the background of the novel.

NICHOLAS JOSE: Well, the novel evolved from ideas I had when I went to China, to teach Australian studies, in early 1986. Basically, it weaves together a tangle of stories set mostly in Beijing in 1986. The main strand concerns an Australian cancer specialist, Wally Frith, who goes to China in search of non-Western approaches to the disease. His wife has just died from cancer, you see. In the course of events, he falls in love with a Chinese woman, but ends up returning to Australia alone, to continue his work. Running alongside Wally Frith's story are the stories of other Beijingers, local and expatriate, which culminate in the eruption of protest demonstrations in Tiananmen Square in December 1986.

I: And how did the novel become a film?

NJ: Well, the draft of the novel was completed by the end of 1987. My agent showed it to an independent Sydney-based screen producer, who was keen to turn it into a film. This was 18 months before the more famous Tiananmen Square demonstrations of April–June 1989. In the meantime I had accepted an appointment at the Australian Embassy, Beijing, which meant that the revision and editing of the novel was delayed and not scheduled for publication until mid-1989. Then the student movement, unfolding on television around the world, gave a fresh impetus to the project, and the production company commissioned a writer to rework the script in the direction of a political thriller reaching its climax in Tiananmen Square.

I: Tiananmen Square 1989, not 1986.

NJ: Exactly.

I: And what other changes did they make?

NJ: Well, the hero, Australian Wally Frith became Englishman Will Flint. Then the title of the novel, the somberly ironic 'Avenue of Eternal Peace', was changed to 'Children of the Dragon', which comes from a pop song that was sung in the square at the time. You see, the script-writer moved the focus onto youth – it is the doctor's son, not his wife, who has died, for example. And in the ending Wally -rather, Will – rescues a girl student, and they escape to Australia on a jumbo jet – a happier ending, perhaps, than in the original novel.

I: Of course, the film wasn't made in China.

NJ: No, the original plan to film in Beijing had to be abandoned, and it was shot largely in Australia, using many of the thousands of Chinese students who had flocked there in 1989 as extras. One of them appeared on set at the reconstruction of Tiananmen Square wearing the same clothes he had worn to demonstrate in the real square in Beijing – and was told to go home and change into something less colourful!

I: I gather it wasn't easy to find the right actors for the main parts.

NJ: No, casting proved quite difficult. Because the film was an international co-production, you get Bob Peck playing an Englishman working in Australia, with Australian actor Linda Cropper playing the American Monica, a character invented for the film in order to attract American interest. But the production gave opportunities to a great many local Chinese performers – some of them real discoveries.

Unit 11

RECORDING 1   Colour therapy

INTERVIEWER: Tell us a bit about colour therapy, Dr Crystal.

DR CRYSTAL: Well, as its name indicates, it's a form of healing, and it's now being extensively used world wide in one form or another. You are probably aware, for example, that working in an environment of a particular colour can enhance productivity and so on.

I: Could you elaborate on that?

DC: Well, clinical studies have shown how green, for example, promotes overall healing, and is used, therefore, in the design of hospitals. Red, on the contrary, is a stimulating colour, and should be avoided where there is a danger of aggravating mental disturbances. Blue, on the other hand, acts as a pacifier – it has exactly the opposite affect from red. And orange – orange is a good colour for the work place since it improves productivity, while yellow is conducive to thought and mental work.

I: But colour therapy takes this a step further, I gather?

DC: That's right. Colour therapy involves use of specific colours found in foods to treat illnesses, through, for example, the eating of different coloured foods.

I: Like carrots, for example?

DC: Well, yes, carrots are just one example.

I: What are carrots good for?

DC: Well, all orange foods – carrots, pumpkins, erm, apricots …

I: Oranges?

DC: Oranges, peaches and so on, these are good for stimulating the heart, to strengthen the bones and teeth, as well as being very good for lung problems, for example.

I: So how do you know what the different colours are good for?

DC: Well, basically, the colours are divided into either stimulating colours or sedating colours. Orange is a stimulating colour. As is red. Blue, on the other hand, is a sedating colour.

I: Green?

DC: Green and purple are sort of mid-way between. They are very balanced colours.

I: So, what are stimulating colours good for, for example?

DC: Well, what they are not good for is when the patient is already excited, for example, in the case of fever or emotionally agitated and so on. Conversely, sedating colours are not good for depressive conditions. The actual details of colour therapy are quite complicated, and require considerable study. But to give you an example, blue is good for burns, emotional disorders, stress and so on.

I: And what is a blue food?

DC: Well, grapes are blue, prunes, blueberries.

I: So, if I'm feeling stressed, I should eat a bowl of prunes?

DC: Well, that might help, yes. But not if you're feeling depressed – blue is a downer, not an upper.

I: So if you're feeling blue, avoid the blues?

DC: Exactly.

I: Well, let's say I have a bit of a stomach problem. What should I take?

DC: Well, if it's a case of an upset stomach, yellow is the colour for that.

I: And what's yellow food? Corn?

DC: Yes, corn is very good. Bananas, lemons, eggs.

I: Tomatoes?

DC: No, tomatoes are red. Along with cherries, beets, and so on.

I: And what are red things good for?

DC: Blood problems, like anaemia, for instance. Blood circulation generally. Red helps get things moving.

I: Well, it sounds quite easy really – red for blood, yellow for stomach, but not blue for the blues.

Unit 13

RECORDING 1   OCD

INTERVIEWER: What exactly is OCD?

PSYCHOLOGIST: OCD stands for Obsessive-Compulsive-Disorder. It's a kind of neurosis which manifests itself in obsessive behaviour – behaviour that completely takes over the life of the person suffering from it.

I: For example?

P: Well, a common form of OCD stems from a fear of dirt, of contamination, with the result that the sufferer becomes a 'washer' – they wash themselves literally hundreds of times a day, often to the point that their skin cracks or bleeds. 'Washers' are probably the most common form of obsessive. There are also what we call 'checkers' – people who obsessively check locks, doors, windows, lights and so on, again, maybe hundreds of times a day.

I: Is this a common condition?

P: Commoner than you would think. In the United States, for example, it's been estimated that between four and five million people suffer from it.

I: What sort of people get it?

P: Anybody really. But it tends to occur with people who have always been a bit – how can I put it? – a bit fussy, perfectionists, you know? Of course, it's not unusual for anybody to adopt little rituals, habits, like touching wood for good luck and so on. But it's when these rituals start taking over your life that the condition becomes a disorder. It's often triggered by a bout of depression.

I: Can it be cured?

P: Well, twenty years or so ago, there wasn't much treatment at all. If you were lucky you might be left to get worse. If you were unlucky you might be given electric shock therapy or a lobotomy – both very risky forms of treatment, with serious side-effects. More recently, the outlook has improved with the introduction of behaviour therapy, which focuses on helping patients to learn to control and, hopefully, overcome their compulsive behaviour.

I: Are drugs of any help?

P: It's true that certain drugs do seem to help, particularly antidepressant drugs. But drug treatment may not be effective unless it's combined with deliberate changes in behaviour. And what often happens is that once the drug treatment is stopped, the compulsive behaviour recurs. Behaviour therapy is really the best form of treatment for this condition.

Unit 15

RECORDING 3   Environmental concerns

1: Well I'm very worried about the destruction of wildlife. I think we're all very selfish and greedy in the way we treat the world. The thing that really hit my imagination very hard was when I saw a programme about the huge five mile lines that they use just to catch tuna fish because we all seem to be so keen on eating endless amounts of tuna fish which are destroying most of the other fish in the sea including dolphins. And I guess I just have a very good feeling about dolphins and it hit my imagination that we should be killing off these creatures just because of our greed and our love of tuna fish. So now I find it very difficult to eat tuna fish unless the tin says 'dolphin friendly nets'.

2: I didn't really realise how bad things had gotten in the ocean 'til I went down to Santa Monica beach last year. You know – it's right off by Los Angeles in California. And there's a pier that goes out to the beach and there were signs in three different languages that said you can't swim in the water, that the water will endanger your health. This is a public beach we're talking about. And so I looked down and the water is brown and it's like frothy. It's unbelievable. But there are still kids that are playing in the water. I mean it was so polluted that it was frightening that a beach, you know, a public area that was – I remember it from when I was a kid – that was, you know, incredibly beautiful and clean, that that has become so unbelievably filthy. And